Planemakers: 4

SHORTS

Michael J. H. Taylor

JANE'S

Sir Philip Foreman, Chairman and Managing Director of Short Brothers (right), shakes hands with EMBRAER's Chairman Eng Ozires Silva, after the announcement in May 1984 of co-operation towards the manufacture of a developed version of the Brazilian Tucano turbo-prop trainer for possible RAF selection

Copyright © Michael J. H. Taylor 1984

First published in the United Kingdom in 1984 by
Jane's Publishing Company Limited
238 City Road, London EC1V 2PU

Distributed in the USA and its dependencies by
Jane's Publishing Inc.
135 West 50th Street
New York NY 10020

ISBN 0 7106 0237 5

Typesetting by
D. P. Media Limited, Hitchin, Hertfordshire

Printed in the United Kingdom by
Biddles Ltd, Guildford, Surrey

Contents

Introduction

Short Brothers Limited, based in Belfast and under the Chairmanship of Sir Philip Foreman, CBE, DL, is a highly competitive and successful manufacturer of twin-turboprop STOL commuter and military transport aircraft and freighters. Other major business activities for worldwide markets include the production of the Seacat shipborne and related Tigercat land-based surface-to-air missile systems, the man-portable Blowpipe and Javelin anti-aircraft missile systems, the Skeet aerial target drone and the wide-serving Shorland armoured car. Shorts is also a risk-sharing partner with Fokker BV of the Netherlands in the production of the F28 Fellowship airliner, and its successor, the new 7100, manufactures advanced component parts for the Boeing 747 and 757 and is one of the world's major designers and suppliers of large jet engine nose cowls and nacelles. Most recently it has joined with the Brazilian manufacturer EMBRAER to offer a version of the Tucano basic trainer to the RAF and, at the time of writing, was negotiating the production of the Sikorsky Blackhawk as a possible Puma and Wessex replacement for the RAF.

These and earlier activities go some way in explaining why Short Brothers has weathered the 'ups and downs' of the aircraft industry over a period of more than three-quarters of a century, during which many famous aviation names just disappeared from the manufacturing scene. Its success has been based upon the philosophy of its founders, the

A Seacat surface-to-air missile blasts from its shipboard launcher. It equips vessels of the Royal Navy and fifteen foreign navies

5

Skeet aerial target drone on its launch rail

Right: Blowpipe is shoulder fired from its carrying/launch container and is optically aimed. It is an effective counter to oncoming attack aircraft, including helicopters, and can be used in a surface-to-surface role

brothers Horace, Eustace and Oswald Short, who were always prepared to adapt to the continually changing aviation requirements of their day. Indeed, the company itself had only been established as an aeroplane manufacturer after Oswald had reportedly commented to Eustace, in 1908, 'this is the finish of ballooning', said at a time when the two brothers were enjoying considerable success as balloon entrepreneurs during the so-called 'golden age of ballooning'. Within a few weeks Horace had joined them to form an aeroplane company.

Over the many years of its existence Short Brothers has been steered to produce very diverse types of aircraft, suited to military or commercial service or experimentation. The biplanes and monoplanes built for early pioneering aviators gave way to large military biplanes (usually seaplanes) to serve in the First World War, and some success was achieved also in the field of non-rigid and rigid airships. After the war Shorts followed a lean period, during which its newly designed aircraft remained prototypes, with the development of large multi-engined flying-boats to operate long over-sea routes with Imperial Airways and equip the military as sea-going patrol aircraft. More than any other aircraft type, Short Brothers is readily associated with the flying-boat.

With war clouds appearing again over Europe in the late 1930s, Shorts developed its Stirling bomber and Sunderland, the latter regarded by many as Britain's finest flying-boat of all time. The former became the first Allied four-engined bomber of the Second World War. When peace returned in 1945, it quickly became clear that the era of the flying-boat for commercial use was drawing to a close, although work on converting ex-military craft for civil operation took place together with some new production. Eventually Shorts turned, after reorganisation (as detailed later), to such advanced projects as jet bombers, verticaltake-off and other experimental aircraft. The last large aircraft to come from the company was the Belfast, a huge transport which gave the RAF the capability of operating on a global basis. Defence spending economies subsequently led to the sale of RAF Belfasts and today a few can be seen only in commercial operation. While the relatively small current Shorts 330, 360, Sherpa and Skyvan are modest when compared to the company's products of the past, they too have set remarkable new standards in their class.

Short Brothers can claim to be the oldest aeroplane manufacturer in the United Kingdom, but this is just one of several historical facts of importance due the company. In 1909 Short Brothers became the first company in the world to put an aeroplane into series production, in the first purpose-built aeroplane factory in Britain; a Short pusher biplane was the first aeroplane to take-off from a moving ship, in 1912; the first naval aircraft with a proper wing-folding mechanism and the first to launch a standard naval torpedo were both Short tractor biplanes. These are but a few of many historic achievements recorded by Short aircraft.

The story of the brothers Short and their eventual part in aviation history begins on 2 July 1872, when Emma Short presented Samuel Short with a son. Named Horace Leonard, he was to be the main force behind the early aeroplane constructing enterprise when in his mid-30s. Unfortunately, at a very young age, Horace suffered an injury to his head which brought on meningitis. Although his head became an abnormal size, his very high intellect clearly helped him cope with this abnormality. Indeed, while still in his teens he set out to work his way to Australia. His adventures *en route* were as if taken from a story book and included his capture and subsequent escape from cannibals. Eventually Horace found his way to Mexico where, as the manager of a silver mine, he used all his cunning together with his rather alarming appearance to keep local outlaws from the silver as it was being transported. His inventive mind was also hard at work during this period and at about this time he invented the Auxetophone, a device by which spoken or pre-recorded sound could be amplified.

The second of the Short brothers was Albert Eustace, always known by his second name. Born in June 1875, as the male head of the Short family living at home after his father died, it was he who (also in his teens) set out with little money to bring Horace home. In 1895 Eustace finally found Horace and thereafter gained a promise from Horace that he would leave Mexico when his work allowed. Eustace, satisfied his mission was complete and with a large sum of money from Horace to aid

Left: Horace Leonard
Short aged 28, testing his
Auxetophone

Shorland armoured cars,
currently serving in
thirteen countries

Hugh Oswald Short pointing towards the camera in 1928 from the bow of an Imperial Airways' Calcutta flying-boat, with John Lankester Parker in the pilot's seat and Winston Churchill to his left

Right: Albert Eustace Short, whose purchase of a second-hand coal gas balloon started the brothers on their aviation career

the family situation, returned to England. With the third brother, Hugh Oswald (born 16 January 1883), still of school age but having to earn money for his mother while his two elder brothers were abroad, Eustace used Horace's money to set up a business as a coal merchant. In 1896 Horace arrived back in England and the family subsequently moved to London. It was here that the Short brothers' interest in aviation germinated.

Back in 1893 Oswald, then about 10 years old and living at the former family home in Derby with his mother and Eustace, had become excited by the rare sight of a free flying balloon drifting over his home. Now in London, he and Eustace became interested in ballooning and in 1897 or 1898 (the former date usually being taken as correct but Oswald later wrote that he was 15 years old at the time, which indicates 1898) Eustace purchased a second-hand Spencer coal-gas balloon named *Queen of the West* at very modest cost because of its poor condition. Over a period of time Eustace and Oswald repaired the balloon and this experience was to set them in good stead for future events. One of the first ascents in the balloon was at a local village gala, when the brothers charged £15 for the sight of seeing Eustace, Horace and a certain Arthur Williams fly a distance of about 64 km (40 miles) at rapid speed. Oswald, always called 'The Kid' by Horace, was not give the chance to fly on this occasion and the rather heavy landing only confirmed to 'down-to-earth' Horace that ballooning was dangerous. However, not pt off, Oswald became a passenger on the next flight.

Not to be persuaded otherwise, Horace left his two younger brothers and set up a laboratory in Hove to work on his Auxetophone. Meanwhile, Eustace and Oswald continued to fly their Spencer balloon for reward, sometimes at festivals and occsionally for wealthy acquaintances. This was in or about 1899. Eustace and Oswald had virtually become showmen but neither forgot the more serious experimental side of ballooning.

The great Paris Exhibition of 1900 attracted all three Short brothers. Horace went to Paris to demonstrate his sound device from the top of the Eiffel Tower, which proved extremely successful, but the mission of his brothers was entirely different. Realising that *Queen of the West* was both old and rather basic in design, Eustace and Oswald had begun designing their own balloon – it is believed that actual construction of this above Horace's laboratory did not start until 20 April 1901. Their interest in the Paris Exhibition was to view the beautifully constructed French balloons manufactured by Astra Société de Constructions Aeronautique of Billancourt. Astra had been founded by Edouard Surcouf for the production of (according to the 1913 *Jane's All the World's Aircraft*) 'ordinary balloons' but from 1903 was to become famous for its airships. The Shorts were particularly interested in the company's method of producing balloons with spherical envelopes.

On returning to England in 1900, Eustace and Oswald reworked their balloon and this was completed in May 1901. Undoubtedly used to continue some fund-raising activities, this first-ever Short aircraft was said by Oswald to have been 12.5 metres (41 ft) in diameter. At about this time Horace sold his patents in the Auxetophone and took employment in the north of England as an engineer. Eustace and Oswald, having had good results from their first project, were encouraged to continue with balloon manufacture and searched for new premises. Although many accounts of these early days mention the brothers occupying premises under railway arches, this is considered by the author to be chronologically incorrect. Having had to move out of Horace's laboratory building, Eustace and Oswald used their mother's house in what was then Saville Street, Langham Street West, as a business address and occupied a carriage shed in the London Mews off the Tottenham Court Road. The exact date of opening is not clear but it was in 1902. Here they constructed their second balloon for display work, a captive balloon thought to have been of about 1,700 m³ (60,000 cu ft) volume. Unfortunately this balloon had an envelope that leaked gas and was not a success.

1904 brought changes of fortune to Eustace and Oswald and saw the brief return of their inventive brother Horace. It was probably Eustace (in about 1902) who hit upon the idea of designing and constructing a vast 17,698 m³ (625,000 cu ft) balloon for high-altitude flying, lifting an airtight and pressurised spherical gondola made from aluminium. Such a project was bound to interest Horace and indeed he later became involved in designing the pressurisation system and other aspects of the gondola, which included a downward-projecting periscope for viewing. Sure that such a project would interest the Aeronautical Society of Great Britain (founded in 1866), Horace and Eustace gave a lecture on the subject of airtight gondolas for high-altitude ascents and other aspects of the balloon in July 1904. However, the project raised little real interest and no sponsor was forthcoming. Thus ended Horace's interest in his brothers' ballooning activities.

The earlier failure of their second balloon, especially in view of the fact that they had not been able to fulfil a much needed contract from the New Brighton Tower Company at Blackpool to fly the balloon, and the lack of support for their high-altitude project, could have prolonged (in Oswald's words) 'a dark and sombre period' had other events not taken place to soften these blows. By the time of the lecture, Eustace and Oswald had already answered an advertisement placed by the War Office in *The Times* newspaper to tender for a contract to construct balloons for the government of India. The initial contract had been received in October 1903 and others followed. These balloons were intended for reconnaissance work with the Indian Army. These were the first Short brothers' aircraft to be sold.

The hallmark of these balloons was high quality, giving the brothers an enviable reputation that was to continue into the later aeroplane manufacturing business (still some years away). Before going to India, the balloons were inspected by Colonel J. L. B. Templer, who was running the HM Balloon Factory at Farnborough. His high praise for the quality of workmanship was indeed welcomed. Templer had been involved in the development of balloons for the British Army since 1878, when the sum of £150 had been allocated by the War Office for the construction of a balloon (the first) for the British Army. Captain Templer, then of the Middlesex Militia, and another captain, were given the task of carrying out development work and Templer later became the first ever British Air Commander. The Balloon School and Factory were moved to Farnborough in 1891. More important than Templer's words to the Short brothers were his introductions to well-known Aero Club aeronauts. One such man was Charles S. Rolls, who ordered a balloon from the Shorts for use in the first ever Gordon Bennett International Balloon Race. The resulting balloon was named *Britannia* and took part in the 1906 race for a trophy and a cash prize. In this race of sixteen balloons that ascended from Tuileries, Paris, only three managed to cross the English Channel, Rolls' *Britannia* among them. Rolls reached Norfolk but in the event came in second to the US Army aeronaut Lt Frank Lahm who, flying the balloon *United States*, landed at Fylingdales, Yorkshire, after covering a distance of 647 km (402 miles).

Britannia was one of three balloons ordered at this early stage for members of the Aero Club, the others being *Zephyr* for Professor A. Huntingdon and *Venus* for the joint ownership of Charles Rolls, J. T. C. Moore-Brabazon and Warwick Wright. Although documentary evidence concerning the exploits of Eustace and Oswald in their balloon manufacturing venture is easier to come by for the period from 1906, there still remain several grey areas. One such area is the exact date the brothers left their carriage shed and moved to two railway arches rented at Battersea Park from the London Brighton and South Coast Railway. This was in June 1906, the month after *Venus* had flown for the first time. Certainly the brothers required the extra space these arches afforded them, as well as the grounds suited for ascents. Another bonus was the adjacent gas works. A further area of doubt comes in the timing that found the brothers appointed officially as the aeronautical engineers to the Aero Club. It has been quoted that they received this title after winning a gold medal for 'Excellence of Construction' with an exhibited balloon at an Aero Club exhibition in 1907. In fact the Short balloon received such a prize in March 1906. In a newspaper report published on 3 August 1906, the Short brothers are mentioned as manufacturers to the Aero Club and that they had lately acquired premises at the Battersea Gasworks. At this time the brothers charged between £120 and £400 for a balloon and, as part of their business, they would prepare a balloon for flight for an inclusive price of about £8.

During 1907 and 1908 Eustace and Oswald built up a thriving business at Battersea, not only producing balloons to order but maintaining them and preparing balloons for flight in 'double quick' time for those wishing to take advantage of good weather for an aerial journey over Battersea and London. Incredibly, it appears that the Shorts only employed one person during this period, a Miss Prince, whose job it was to sew the balloon envelopes. Much of each balloon must have been, therefore, sub-contracted out. This period was one of extreme pleasure for the two brothers who, by Oswald's own admission, did not possess 'any particular business acumen' and constructed the balloons as 'a labour of love to us'. Certainly the quality of their products bore out the latter sentiment, when the Shorts 'spared neither pains nor expense in executing it'.

The Short brothers' first venture into heavier-than-air craft also came while at Battersea. In 1907 J. T. C. Moore-Brabazon (already a user of a Short balloon and who later became Lord Brabazon of Tara) had attempted to become airborne in a glider at Brooklands. This aircraft had been assembled by the Short brothers. Unsuccessful as a glider, Moore-Brabazon and Warwick modified it into a powered aircraft but it remained a failure. However, in 1909 Moore-Brabazon established himself as the foremost English aeroplane pilot when, during April and May, he flew a French Voisin biplane to become the first resident Englishman to undertake an officially recognised flight in an aeroplane in England. His many later exploits in heavier-than-air craft included taking a pig aloft in an aeroplane, thus proving that pigs could fly!

Eustace and Oswald continued their balloon business after work on the Moore-Brabazon glider but events overseas were about to have direct influence on them and cause a change in their careers. On 6 May 1908 the famous American Wright brothers began flying again after a self-imposed absence of nearly three years. Although by then their *Flyer* biplane had lost technical ground to some European aeroplanes being tested, in its further developed form it was still capable of outflying all comers and so the Wrights accepted invitations to demonstrate their aircraft in France. As things turned out Wilbur Wright journeyed from the USA to Europe, leaving his brother Orville the responsibility of the preparations for the US military trials that were to take place at Fort Myer from September onwards. It was while undertaking these trials that Orville crashed (on 17 September) and was badly injured.

Meanwhile, on 8 August Wilbur began flying at Hunaudières in France using a small racecourse a few miles from Le Mans, his aeroplane being a Model A two-seater. The first demonstration flight lasted 1 minute 45 seconds. Having transferred to Camp d'Auvours on 21

Left: *Britannia*, constructed for Charles Rolls, was supplied with two baskets, one to accommodate two persons while racing and this much larger basket for up to ten persons for pleasure flights

Short Brothers' famous works at the Battersea railway arches in 1909, with *Venus* and *Continental 2* being prepared for flight

August (a course east of Le Mans), on 21 September he performed the first significant endurance flight in an aeroplane ever, by remaining airborne over a distance of 66.5 km (41.3 miles). On 8 October he took up as passenger a gentleman by the name of Griffith Brewer, then the Wrights' Patent agent for Great Britain and member of the Aero Club. Brewer thus became the first Briton to fly as a passenger in an aeroplane. Many other persons were taken up by Wilbur during his period in Europe, including other members of the Aero Club.

Because of their close association with the Aero Club, the Short brothers soon heard good reports of Wilbur Wright's flying in France. While not abandoning their balloon business outright, Eustace and Oswald quickly came to the historic decision to branch into aeroplane construction. But, clearly for this they would benefit from their elder brother's inventive genius. Oswald set off to Newcastle-upon-Tyne to approach Horace and must have been surprised by his immediate willingness to participate. Indeed, Horace warned Oswald that he would go into the aeroplane business alone if his two brothers were not prepared by the time he arrived at Battersea. Horace managed to obtain a release from his newly signed contract with Parsons, where he had been working as an engineer, receiving his last pay packet two days before Christmas.

The Short Brothers partnership was agreed in late 1908. Eustace had probably already been to Le Mans to see the Wright biplane in flight and it was on his second such journey that he became the first of the Short brothers to fly in a powered aeroplane. This came about on 5 December 1908, having gone to France as the official engineer representing members of the Aero Club who had formed a syndicate in the hope of purchasing from the Wrights the UK patent rights in the Model A. In this wish the syndicate was not successful, as the Wrights considered the British market too limited for such an agreement, although this decision was not reached until early in 1909.

Soon after Eustace's journey, a powered aeroplane to be designed by Short Brothers was ordered by Frank McClean (who had also flown with Wilbur in France). Horace, who designed the aeroplane, must have been proud that his brothers' reputation for quality of workmanship on balloons had led so quickly to this first order for the new company.

While work on the Short No 1 commenced, Wilbur Wright continued to give excellent demonstrations in France. While there can be little doubt that the Wrights were attempting to capitalise financially on their aeroplane design, still no series production line had been established in Britain to satisfy the many inquiries for similar aircraft. In February 1909 the Wrights decided to award a contract for limited production of their aircraft in Britain and, following a conversation between Wilbur and Griffith Brewer, Short Brothers was approached as the possible British manufacturer. It was decided that the contract should cover six machines.

Returning briefly to 1908, on 31 December Wilbur had won the Michelin prize with a flight of 124 km (77 miles), his final flight at Camp d'Auvours before moving south to Pau to take advantage of better weather. Therefore, it was to Pau that Horace journeyed to prepare drawings of the Wright machine in preparation for the construction of the Short-Wrights in England. By now Orville had joined his brother in France. A further Wright-designed aircraft was also to be constructed by Shorts, comprising a glider ordered by Charles Rolls in May 1909 so that he could begin heavier-than-air flight training in preparation for the receipt of a Short-Wright powered machine. In fact Rolls had been so anxious to purchase a powered Wright aeroplane that as early as September 1908 he had ordered a machine from Wilbur, before any decision had been reached as to its source of manufacture.

Work on the Short No 1 for Frank McClean started in February 1909 at the Battersea arches and in March the unfinished airframe, without an engine but with propellers fitted, was exhibited at the Olympia show. Soon after this the glider for Rolls was put in hand, possibly at Battersea, and this became the first Short aircraft to be tested in 1909.

Meanwhile, prominent Aero Club member Griffith Brewer had been attempting to find suitable ground from which McClean could fly his Short No 1 when completed. He was subsequently attracted by marsh-land near the village of Leysdown on the Isle of Sheppey, Kent. As a result, McClean purchased a farmhouse for the Aero Club to use together with the rights to fly over 350 acres of land. Short Brothers purchased a plot on the same site where the company set up its first purpose-built workshop, construction starting in February 1909, shortly before a contract was signed (in March) for the Short-Wrights. The flying area of the Aero Club was known as Shellbeach and was available for members only. It was in the Short Brothers' new workshop that final completion of the glider for Rolls took place, together with the process of covering the No 1 aeroplane with fabric and construction of the Short-Wrights. It is interesting that while it was not necessary for the Short brothers to maintain silence regarding the receipt of the contract from the Wright brothers, it was Griffith Brewer who first brought the

Short No 1 biplane under construction at the Battersea works in 1909

news to the attention of the press on about 16 March 1909, just days after the Leysdown works had been completed. Indeed, it appears that the Short brothers were anxious not to gain prominence on the basis of their business connection with the world famous Wrights alone. The contract was worth £1,200 and all six machines were sooner or later committed to members of the Aero Club.

Despite their new interest in aeroplanes, Eustace and Oswald also continued the balloon business at Battersea in 1909, leaving Horace to control the aeroplane side. A final cessation to the construction of gas balloons at Battersea only came with the outbreak of the First World War, which effectively put an end to the delivery of envelope material from their German supplier. However, in 1915 the Admiralty decided it required, as a matter of some urgency, large numbers of small non-rigid airships to counter German U-boats. These, designated SS (Submarine Scout) types, were intended for patrol and convoy duties; by the end of the war 139 SS airships had been completed for service. The first SS airships to be built were the *SS2* and *SS3*, constructed by Airships Ltd and Short Brothers respectively (*SS1* having been a conversion of the Willows IV, later modified into the 1,104 m³ [39,000 cu ft] Naval Airship No 2 by Airships Ltd). The 1,982 m³ (70,000 cu ft) *SS2* was not successful but *SS3*, the first of the actual production series, proved excellent. Despite this, Airships Ltd was given contracts to produce 12 more and it appears likely that Armstrong Whitworth built nine. The Admiralty was responsible for the remainder. Shorts had to be content with the production of small component parts, which were assembled in the Admiralty airships at Kingsnorth and Wormwood Scrubbs. *SS3*, like others in the initial SS series of 26 craft plus the *SS1* and Curtiss-engined *SS2*, had the fuselage of a Royal Aircraft Factory BE 2c aeroplane as the gondola (fitted with a 52 kW; 70 hp Renault engine). Queen's Circus, Battersea Park, continued as a branch of Short Brothers until the early 1920s.

On 3 and 4 May 1909 respectively the Wright brothers visited the Short Brothers' works at Battersea and Leysdown, apparently liking what they saw and the quality of workmanship going into the production of flying machines. During this year Short Brothers also worked on the Huntingdon monoplane, designed by Lt J. W. Dunne originally for the British War Office but assigned to Professor A. K. Huntingdon (sometimes called a triplane because of its strange triple wing layout), and the Dunne V tailless biplane. Both aircraft flew in June 1910 from the Eastchurch flying ground (detailed later). The company also contributed to later Dunne aircraft.

The Leysdown works in 1909 where, in the 140 ft by 45 ft workshop, the Short-Wright biplanes were being constructed. These aircraft were said to have been of much higher quality than the Wright biplanes built in France

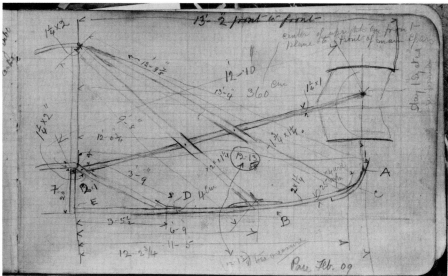

Having journeyed to Pau, Horace made sketches of the Wright biplane in a notebook, from which plans were drawn

The Wright brothers,
Griffith Brewer and
Charles Rolls journeyed to
the Leysdown works on 4
May 1909 by Rolls-Royce
motor car

A report published in a prominent aviation magazine in mid-August 1909 stated that Short Brothers then employed about 80 men, this going on to say that Orville Wright was due to test the Wright *Flyers* built by Shorts in a few days. Unfortunately, the publication had no way of knowing then that the power plants, ordered from the licenced French manufacturer of Wright engines, had not arrived in England and so no testing could take place. Another two months were to pass before the first Short-Wright flew. The first machine went to Charles Rolls who, from November 1909, began a series of prize-winning flights. Eventually Rolls received two Short-Wrights, as well as a French-built Wright constructed by Astra Cie; French production of the Wright biplane was far greater than British and these aircraft differed from US/British models originally by having wheeled landing gears and a horizontal surface to the rear of the two vertical surfaces. It was in his French Wright that Rolls completed the first ever double crossing of the English Channel, on 2 June 1910. However, Rolls was to die tragically only five weeks later, on 12 July 1910, after a crash during the Bournemouth Aviation Week meeting.

It appears that Short Brothers was offered the opportunity of producing further Wright biplanes under licence but Horace declined. This can be seen, in retrospect, partly as an indication of Horace's faith in his own abilities as an aeroplane designer. For, although the first Short biplane had not been successful, No 2 had shown much more promise, not least because it was on this machine that Moore-Brabazon won the *Daily Mail* £1,000 prize as the first Briton to fly for one mile in a British aeroplane, on 30 October 1909. However, another factor in the decision was that the Short-Wright was out of date even before the last was delivered (in 1910); Horace probably realised this to be the case in late 1909, especially after the success of French-designed aircraft during the Reims International Meeting of August.

From May 1910 the Royal Aero Club (as it had become in February) began using a new 350 acre site at Eastchurch, having found Shellbeach too hazardous. Short Brothers established a new works adjacent to the site and it was here that a series of successful pusher biplanes was constructed, including what were probably the world's first successful multi-engined aeroplanes. Shorts at Eastchurch also produced the bi-

planes on which the first four officers appointed by the Admiralty to the Royal Flying Corps, Naval Wing, were taught to fly. A Naval flying school was formed at Eastchurch in December 1911.

In 1912 Short Brothers took up the design of seaplanes and, according to the *Jane's All the World's Aircraft* of the time, 'achieved almost immediate success'. Meanwhile, on 10 January 1912 Lt (later Colonel) Charles Rumney Samson took off in the Short S.38 biplane (fitted with emergency flotation bags) from the specially built wooden platform on board HMS *Africa*, so recording the first launch of an aeroplane from a British ship. On 9 May the same year Samson became the first airman ever to fly an aeroplane from a moving ship, when he piloted the Short biplane from the platform transferred to the battleship HMS *Hibernia*, during the Naval Review off Portland.

Shorts' Eastchurch works (at the top of the photograph) in July 1912, with Frank McClean's house 'Stonefitts' (centre left) and sheds belonging to the Royal Aero Club

HMS *Hibernia* in May 1912, with final preparations being made before Samson was to attempt take off

H.M.S.'Hibernia', with SHORT Biplane 'S.38' on special platform

With the introduction of the Short Patent Folding Wing device in 1913, the firm revolutionised the usefulness of seaplanes, making it possible for seaplanes of large dimensions to be carried in Royal Navy ships for operations in all parts of the world. The device also offered important savings in the cost of storage of both seaplanes and landplanes. Rapidly Shorts found its seaplane work becoming its most important and, with expanding business, the company erected new works at Rochester in Kent (with an address as Willis Avenue), ideal for launching seaplanes by virtue of being situated on one bank of the river

Aerial view of the Rochester works on the river Medway

Medway. This new site was placed under the charge of 'The Kid' Oswald.

The outbreak of the First World War brought urgency to the production of aircraft for the flying services and Shorts was well placed to provide important large seaplanes. Equally important to the success of the company at this time was the nearby Royal Dockyard, from which Shorts gained trained labour and skilled design and technical personnel: in 1913 Short Brothers had employed about 100 persons, but this figure quickly increased.

A Short seaplane was the first British aircraft to be employed successfully in a naval engagement, as can be construed from this extract of an official letter to Messrs Short Brothers:

> '. . . the flight made by Flight Lieut. Rutland, with Assistant Paymaster Trewin, as observer, which Sir David Beatty praises so highly, was carried out on a 225-h.p. "Short Seaplane" . . .'

The action mentioned above was that on 31 May 1916, when the Short Admiralty Type 184 in question was flown form HMS *Engadine* and spotted and then shadowed German warships before the Battle of Jutland. The Short Admiralty Type 184 was undoubtedly the company's most important contribution to the war effort. Earlier, on 12 August 1915, a Type 184 flown by Flt Cdr C. H. Edmonds, RNAS, from HMS *Ben-My-Chree*, had carried out the first ever air attack with a torpedo, sinking a Turkish supply ship in the Sea of Marmara during the Dardanelles campaign. On the 17th Edmonds sank a second Turkish vessel and his colleague, Flt Lt G. B. Dacre, also destroyed a Turkish boat (a tug) with a torpedo, having released it from his aircraft while taxiing on the water because of mechanical problems.

At the close of 1915, owing to the rapid development of its business, Short Brothers found it necessary to establish an office in London. It was at 29/30 Charing Cross, London SW, from where the 'business' side of the company's activities was mainly carried out. The manager of this office was J. P. Parker, formerly Assistant-Paymaster, Royal Navy, afterwards one of the best pilots of the RNAS before being invalided out of the Service before the outbreak of the war. Another Parker came on to the scene soon after, in 1916. Since 1912 Short Brothers had used the part-time services of Gordon Bell as the company's first employed test pilot. In August 1914 Ronald Kemp took over as test pilot but such was the volume of work by 1916 that several other pilots were employed on a casual basis. By the autumn the number of aircraft ready for flight had again stretched the capacity of the testers and a new assistant pilot was sent for named John Lankester Parker. On seeing the young age of this pilot, Horace would not allow him to fly the waiting Short Bombers. However, when faced with Parker's resignation, Horace warned him he would break his neck and then left the site. That day and the next, 17 and 18 October 1916, Parker flew all six new Bombers and Horace had to admit that he was indeed a fine pilot. From 1918 until about the end of the Second World War, Parker was the chief test pilot at Shorts. He is recognised as having been one of the world's greatest flying-boat pilots and is credited with having flown every Short prototype during this period and well into the Second World War. He also became a Director of the company, a position he held into the 1950s and was awarded the OBE.

During the First World War, Short Brothers had its products built under licence by other companies and constructed aircraft not of its design, as detailed in the main section of this book. The company also returned briefly to lighter-than-air craft after producing *SS3*, when its bid to construct two new rigid airships for the Admiralty was accepted. For the construction of these craft, designated *R31* and *R32*, Shorts was given a government loan to put up a massive airship shed at Cardington near Bedford. *R31* and *R32* had wooden structures, their design being based upon Schütte-Lanz principles furnished by the Admiralty who, in turn, had gained the information from a Swiss engineer. *R31* was damaged beyond repair in a rainstorm in November 1918, having logged some 9 hours in the air, caused when the airship had to be landed during its delivery flight and was thereafter housed for too long unattended in a shed at Howden that lacked a roof. It was sold as scrap for £200. *R32* proved much more successful and remained in service until deleted in 1921, when the Airship Service was shut down.

While building *R31* and *R32*, Shorts increased its activities at Cardington by taking over from Vickers the assembly of the duralumin-framed *R37* in 1917. Two months before the end of the war Shorts also received a contract for the construction of the *R38*. After the Armistice, construction of all airships in Britain virtually came to an end, although Vickers went on to complete its *R80* in 1920. A conference was held thereafter by leading British airship builders to propose the formation of a Commercial Airship Combine, to take over surplus military airships and operate them on selected trans-ocean routes for passenger and mail services in combination with certain large steamship companies. The plan did not materialise, however, due to lack of support from the shipping companies. The ex-military airships in question, and presumably others in building, were those which could not be operated by or purchased for the postwar Airship Service, as this British force had been reduced practically to a nucleus formation amounting to one permanent and manned station at Howden. In addition to this difficult situation, the Cardington aircraft works belonging to Shorts was taken over compulsorily for the Airship Service in April 1919 as an experimental station, with compensation to Shorts. This fate can, in retrospect, be viewed as slightly better for Shorts than that which befell Armstrong Whitworth, which had its airship works closed entirely.

As a result of these events, the *R37* was never completed and *R38* was built as a Service Airship Factory type, after the contract originally given to Short Brothers had been withdrawn. As the *R38* had been designed for service over the North Sea, with an exceptionally high service ceiling to prevent enemy fighter interception, it incorporated several innovative features. Work on the *R38* had been taken over from Shorts only after some progress had been made. Subsequently, because of the impending closure of the Airship Service, trials with the *R38* were rushed, despite the knowledge that the craft was weak. Then, after having been sold to the US Navy, the *R38* broke up on 24 August 1921. Sixteen of the 49 persons who died were Americans. Short Brothers' early involvement with the *R38* was its last venture into airship construction.

Meanwhile, back in 1915 a famous name in the annals of Short Brothers joined the company, when Arthur Gouge became an employee fitter at Eastchurch. So keen was he to progress in his chosen career that he gained a degree in engineering by attending evening classes. After the war, by which time the Eastchurch works had been handed over to the RNAS, Shorts also enlisted the rather unique talents of aircraft designer and ex-RNAS officer Oscar Gnosspelius, who was put in charge of the new experimental department at Rochester. Gouge was assigned to Gnosspelius and together they began research into the hydrodynamics of metal seaplane floats and flying-boat hulls and their resistance to water corrosion. Unknowingly, this was one of the most important personnel moves the company made in the early postwar period, as Arthur Gouge (later Sir Arthur) was to exert great influence on Short Brothers' aircraft during the 'interwar' period and became a Director of the company, the General Manager and Chief Designer, ending as Vice-Chairman in 1939. He and Oswald also gained the Freedom of the city of Rochester in recognition of their work in the area and their contributions to aviation.

On 6 April 1917, Horace died as a result of an illness, leaving the extensive company business to Eustace and Oswald. It was Oswald who took over Horace's work at Rochester and remained Managing Director of the company throughout the 'interwar' period.

Like many other aircraft manufacturing companies that had grown large as a direct result of war orders, in peacetime Short Brothers found itself without contracts to keep its work force in employment. In 1919 the Short Brothers partnership was incorporated as a Limited Liability Company, becoming Short Brothers (Rochester and Bedford) Ltd with Oswald as Chairman and Joint Managing Director with Eustace. Another famous aircraft company of this period, that of Sopwith,

Barges under construction down river from the Rochester seaplane works, seen at various stages of completion

Short Brothers undertook the construction of hundreds of omnibus bodies over many years as part of its survival programme, these for the London General Omnibus Co

attempted to get around the lack of work problem by manufacturing motorcycles but, in 1920, went into liquidation. To avoid liquidation or at least a massive cut in its work force, Short Brothers undertook the construction of boats and then omnibus bodies, the latter proving the company's salvation for the first decade of peace. Hundreds of these bodies were constructed.

While omnibus production was underway, Short Brothers managed to keep a reduced aircraft division in existence, ready for the day when the climate for orders changed and one of its prototypes attracted military or commercial orders. Although in the event only prototypes were produced for much of the decade, some of these were of major importance and gave the company considerable technical expertise in advanced design and the use of new materials. One such aircraft was the Silver Streak, which appeared in August 1920. This, the first British all-metal aeroplane, was developed partly as the result of circumstances and partly by design. The war of 1914–18 had consumed vast quantities of the world's timber, with the result that plentiful supplies of good aircraft-quality wood were, by 1918, a thing of the past. Short Brothers found this situation more desperate than some other manufacturers, as most of its aeroplanes took off and landed on water and so were exposed to harsh elements. At the end of the war Shorts had also witnessed the dramatic effects of an unsound wooden framework (caused by the glue), with the demise of the *R31* airship. But, having taken on the assembly of the *R37*, the company had gained valuable experience in working with duralumin, a wrought alloy based on aluminium but containing small amounts of copper, magnesium and manganese.

In 1919 Short Brothers began work on the Silver Streak and was much pleased with the result. The importance of this aircraft did not escape others, and the following paragraphs are extracts from the 1922 edition of *Jane's All the World's Aircraft*:

'Short Bros' wide experience in the construction of rigid airships made them familiar with aluminium alloys, and when it became apparent that something more durable than wood and fabric was required in modern aircraft, they started experimenting on duralumin with a view to building with it complete machines as light and strong as, and definitely more durable than, the present types.

The results have been extremely satisfactory and show that for equal weight a higher factor of safety can be obtained with duralumin than with a wooden structure.

The advantage of using non-inflammable material is apparent, and the known deficiencies of wood and fabric aeroplanes, such as distortion and deterioration due to climatic conditions, are obviated.

The fuselage is a metal shell, similar in construction to the wooden monocoque type, and is virtually a streamline duralumin tube suitably stiffened with bulkheads, rings and longitudinals.

. . . The Silver Streak has for some time been in the hands of the R.A.E. at Farnborough for experimental purposes. Flying tests have shown it to possess a really excellent performance, and an extensive series of mechanical tests have proved the structure to possess the necessary strength, together with an extraordinary resistance to long-continued vibrations of a magnitude quite beyond those due to normal use.

The satisfactory result of these tests have been demonstrated by a definite order on the part of the Air Ministry for two further machines embodying the same type of construction.'

Having gained an Air Ministry order for prototypes of a two-seat fighter derivative as a Bristol Fighter biplane replacement, Short Brothers looked set for a production run. This was not to be the case, however, and within a few months even the prototypes had been cancelled. Two years later the first Short flying-boat with a metal hull appeared, as the Stellite. The company's first series production aircraft with a metal fuselage was the famous Calcutta flying-boat, which appeared in 1928.

The 1930s saw a change in the fortunes of the aircraft division, with steady but limited production of large flying-boats for military and commercial use. An interesting 'one-off' of this period appeared in

The Sarafand, Shorts' six-engined flying-boat and the world's second largest aircraft of its time

23

An up-to-date view of the
Short Brothers' Belfast
factories and airfield

June 1932, when Short Brothers flew the prototype Sarafand, then the
world's second largest aeroplane (the German Dornier Do X being the
largest but not as successful in performance). However, before this flew
Eustace had died from a heart attack while landing his beloved Short
Mussel II seaplane, on 8 April. Now only Oswald of the original founding brothers survived to see the company through its best years.

1936 was an important year in the development of Short Brothers. In
June Short & Harland Ltd was formed as a result of an agreement
between Short Brothers (Rochester and Bedford) Ltd and Harland &
Wolff Ltd, the well-known shipbuilders, to form a new company to
build both land and marine aircraft in Belfast, Northern Ireland. It is in
Belfast that Shorts operates today. It is interesting to note that the
contracts for landplanes received before the outbreak of the Second
World War included those for the production of the Bristol Bombay
bomber-transport and Handley Page Hereford bomber.

Also in 1936 (July) the first of the company's 'Empire' flying-boats
appeared, which subsequently became much-loved over-ocean transports in the hands of Imperial Airways. The decision by Imperial
Airways to buy a large number of these aircraft before a single machine
had been built, 'straight off the drawing board', must rank as one of that
airline's greatest gambles but one which paid off handsomely. The last
civil flying-boats of Short design to go into service before the war were

those of the G class Golden Hind series, basically enlarged C class
Empire types. The same year Short Brothers received its first Air
Ministry contracts for the Stirling four-engined bomber, ordered 'off
the drawing board', and series-built Sunderland military flying-boats.

In 1937 Short Brothers produced a flying-boat named *Maia* and the
seaplane *Mercury* which, together, proved a winning combination. Back
in 1935 The Mayo Composite Aircraft Company Ltd had been formed
to acquire and handle the world rights in the Composite Aircraft
invented and patented by Major R. H. Mayo. The Composite concept
was for a very highly loaded aircraft to be mounted on top of another
comparatively lightly loaded aircraft to form a composite aircraft capable of taking off easily and quickly under ordinary conditions. After
climbing to altitude, the upper component would then be released from
the lower to continue on a long-range journey carrying a fuel and freight
load with which it would have been incapable of lifting by itself at
take-off.

This seemingly strange concept was flight-tested using the Short-built
Maia and *Mercury* and details of these aircraft can be found in the main
section of this book. It is sufficient here to say that it was a great success
and in the 1980s *Mercury*, having used the composite take-off method,
still held the distance in a straight line world record for seaplanes: this it
set during 6–8 October 1938 at 5,211.66 nm (9,652 km; 5,997.5
miles), with a flight from Dundee, Scotland, to the Orange River, South

**The Short-Mayo
Composite, comprising
Maia and *Mercury*, takes
off with all eight engines
running**

Africa. *Mercury* and *Maia* are best remembered simply as the Short-Mayo Composite.

During the 1930s Short Brothers also produced landplanes but, as Rochester had been developed as a works mainly for seaplanes and flying-boats, wheeled aircraft had to be disassembled for transportation to a suitable airfield before flight testing could commence. Therefore, when in 1933 the Rochester City Council decided to compulsorily purchase land on which to construct an airport, Shorts was interested in gaining permission to erect a hangar on the site and make use of the facilities. This the company was granted by the lease of some land and, although the lease ran from the beginning of 1934, a Short Scion took off from the airport site on 16 December 1933. Rochester Airport and the Scion were also responsible for the nearest Short Brothers came to establishing an airline when, in order to demonstrate in the most obvious way the attributes of the Scion as a feeder-line light transport, two were flown between this airport and Rochford Aerodrome, Southend, by Short pilots over a period of four months in conjunction with Southend-on-Sea Flying Services. Several flights a day were made, each passenger being charged 8 shillings for a one-way journey and 12 shillings for the return fare. Interestingly, despite Shorts' activities at Rochester Airport in 1934, the airport was not officially opened until the following year. Short Brothers finally gave up its facilities at Rochester Airport on 13 June 1962, although the company's main headquarters had been transferred to Belfast late in 1936 as the war clouds were once again gathering over Europe.

The activities of Short Brothers during the Second World War were mainly concerned with the production of the Stirling bomber and

Sunderland flying-boat; on the night of 10–11 February 1941, No 7 Squadron became the first unit of the RAF to fly four-engined bombers into action on a heavy raid since the 1914–18 war, when it struck Rotterdam with its new Stirlings. Further exploits of these aircraft are given in the appropriate entries in the main section of this book.

In January 1943 Oswald resigned as Managing Director and Short Brothers (Rochester and Bedford) Ltd was taken over by the British government as a war measure that March. Oswald was thereafter appointed Honorary Life President, a position he retained until his death on 4 December 1969.

After the end of the Second World War the Sunderland was widely used for commercial operations, modified to suit its new civil status. In addition to modified Sunderlands used by BOAC as its 'Hythe' class, the Sandringham was also produced by Sunderland conversion. However, the final Short flying-boat of new design was the Sealand, which appeared in 1948 and achieved modest production success.

The geneology of the demise of the flying-boat in Britain can be traced to the autumn of 1944, when the axe was beginning to be sharpened ready for the cutback of military contracts expected with the end of the Second World War. Although it was government policy to ensure that the disastrous effects the withdrawal of military contracts had had on the British aircraft industry in 1918 were not repeated in 1945, little could be done to soften the blow when it came. Only those aircraft manufacturers involved in new technology programmes, such as jet fighter and large land-based airliner production, were safe. Despite BOAC taking major steps towards re-establishing flying-boat services, the era of the commercial flying-boat for long-distance air travel had by

Short-produced Canberra PR.9

then virtually passed. In June 1946 the British press carried the news that the government-run Short company was to shut its Rochester factories and transfer the complete Short business to Belfast. As a result, Short Brothers (Rochester and Bedford) Ltd sold its design and manufacturing business to Short & Harland Ltd but remained the principal shareholder. Thereafter Short Brothers (Rochester and Bedford) Ltd became a holding company as S.B. (Realisations) Ltd and Short & Harland changed its name to Short Brothers & Harland Ltd. By October 1948 the city had seen the last of the firm. This was the end of an era for the company and the city and marked the wind-down of water-borne aircraft in British military and commercial service.

Belfast became the principal home for Shorts thereafter, the company having taken the name Short Brothers and Harland Ltd in 1947 after the Rochester company, Short Brothers (Rochester and Bedford) Ltd and the Belfast company were merged. The final aircraft from Rochester had been the Solent flying-boat *Southsea*, launched in April 1948. Only days later BOAC's Southampton flying-boat terminal was opened officially but on 10 November 1950 BOAC terminated its flying-boat services for good, its Solents, Hythe- and Plymouth-class flying-boats being put up for transfer or sale. However, this did not mark the end of Short flying-boats in commercial service, as a number continued in operation with other carriers. The author was, at a very young age, one passenger who flew on an Aquila Airways' Solent 3 (in mid-1954) while returning from Madeira, having journeyed there on a Solent converted from a Seaford.

A little-known side of Shorts' activities postwar concerned the assembly and erection of aluminium school buildings, from the late 1940s, in an effort to increase accommodation for pupils in Northern Ireland schools following the 1947 Education Act. Short aluminium buildings were also used as hospital extensions and for commercial purposes.

For the 1951 Festival of Britain, held in Belfast, Short aluminium buildings were used as a restaurant and children's creche. After the Festival closed, buildings erected for the event were purchased by

The S.A.4 Sperrin, Britain's second type of four-engined jet bomber to fly

The largest Shorts aircraft currently available is the 36-passenger 360

Shorts and a precision engineering division was established. This subsequently became the Missile Systems Division. An Apprentices' Training School for machine-shop instruction had previously been established.

During the 1950s Shorts joined English Electric, Avro and Handley Page in the production of the Canberra jet bomber for the RAF and was also involved in a varied programme of modification and maintenance of other types of aircraft. Before cancellation following the withdrawal of the Certificates of Airworthiness, Shorts had progressed well with the construction of two de Havilland Comet 2 jet airliners, and on 1 June 1957 the first Short-built Bristol Britannia made its maiden flight, after which further Britannia airliners were built on the Belfast production lines, including many Series 252s/253s for RAF Air Transport Command.

Previously, in 1954, The Bristol Aeroplane Company had acquired a small financial interest in Shorts and two directors of the Bristol company were invited to join the board. Rolls-Royce gained an interest in Shorts after taking over Bristol Aero-Engines, while The Bristol Aeroplane Company itself was absorbed into the British Aircraft Corporation in 1960. For many years thereafter Shorts was owned by the British government, Rolls-Royce and Harland & Wolff. On 1 June 1977 Short Brothers & Harland Ltd became known simply as Short Brothers Ltd and this name remains, with the British government currently owning directly or indirectly 100% of the issued shareholding.

During the 1950s Shorts also became heavily involved in the design and construction of advanced experimental aircraft, typified by the

29

S.B.5 – the low speed highly swept test vehicle for the English Electric Lightning fighter and the S.C.1. The latter was not only the first fixed-wing vertical take-off and landing aircraft to be built in the United Kingdom but was the world's first fixed-wing aircraft to demonstrate successful vertical and horizontal flight and hovering flight. The S.C.1 was flown initially by the remarkable Tom Brooke-Smith who, by virtue of being the Chief Test Pilot for a dozen years from 1948, flew what were perhaps the most extraordinary aircraft ever to come off the drawing boards at Shorts. Another interesting prototype was the S.A.4 Sperrin jet bomber that appeared in the early 1950s. Often spuriously said to have been the first four-engined jet bomber of UK origin, this is not so as the Vickers Valiant flew some three months before the Sperrin, although the Short bomber was built to an earlier specification. That aside, the Sperrin has, and deserves, an important place in aviation history.

As mentioned at the beginning of this introduction, the Shorts organisation is located at Belfast, in Northern Ireland, where the company operates a design and production complex which is one of the best equipped of its kind in Europe. Today Shorts is engaged on a broad-based work programme concentrated in three main areas – aircraft, aero-structures and missiles. Aircraft activities cover the whole area of design, development and manufacture of the company's own aircraft projects and this is the division which is responsible for the highly successful Skyvan STOL transport and wide-body 330 regional airliner – both currently in world-wide service – as well as for the new high-economy 360 36-seat airliner and Sherpa multi-role freighter, the latter recently ordered in quantity for the United States Air Force. In recent years Shorts has also greatly extended its international commitments by undertaking the manufacture of major aircraft components for other producers in Europe and America, and has specialised particularly in the business of jet engine nacelle production. Major companies with which Shorts is collaborating include Boeing, Lockheed and Pratt & Whitney in the USA, and British Aerospace, Fokker BV and Rolls-Royce in Europe. In the missile field Shorts is an acknowledged expert in close-range guided weaponry. Its current range includes the Seacat ship-borne system, its land-based variant, Tigercat, and the shoulder-launched Blowpipe and its successor, Javelin. The company has the distinction of supplying guided weapon systems to more countries than any other British manufacturer, and in 1984 Shorts received the Queen's Award to Industry for the thirteenth time. Under the Chairmanship of Sir Philip Foreman, who is also Managing Director, the company employs about 6,500 persons.

Over 80 years since the founding of the company as a partnership by Horace, Eustace and Oswald Short, it remains true to its long-cherished tradition of sound design and high quality of aircraft construction.

The author would like to thank sincerely all those individuals and organisations that assisted in the preparation of this publication, especially Short Brothers Ltd itself and Mr Gordon Bruce.

MJHT

Aircraft Section

SHORT-WRIGHT GLIDER

First flight: 2 August 1909

Type: Single-seat glider

Notes and Structure: Charles Rolls had been interested in powered heavier-than-air flying since first visiting the Wright brothers in late 1906. Shortly before Wilbur journeyed to France in 1908, Rolls tried unsuccessfully to purchase a replica *Flyer* for his personal use (in June 1908) but was compensated in part by becoming the first Briton to see Wilbur Wright at the Hunaudières flying course in August 1908 and was probably the second member of the Aero Club to fly as Wilbur's passenger on 8 October that year.

Rolls had again requested a Wright aeroplane from Wilbur while in France in September, knowing that the Wrights intended to establish some production in Europe. He also wished to be taught to fly by Wilbur but this was not possible as he already had three French pupils. However, one of these, Count Charles de Lambert, later took on pupils but even then Rolls was sixth in line. This was March 1909, but by May Rolls was still waiting. In order to begin heavier-than-air training without undue delay, on 9 May Short Brothers received an order from Rolls to construct a Wright-type glider. This was delivered on 26 July.

The Short-Wright glider was similar to the Wright Glider No 3 but with upright seating and control arrangements for the pilot instead of the original prone position with hip-cradle control.

The constant-chord biplane wings were of equal span and a forward biplane elevator was fitted. Typically, the aircraft was launched from a ground rail using a trolley, although requiring helpers and an incline for take-off as the catapult launch system of powered machines was not adopted.

Much of the airframe was completed at Battersea in about one month and the fabric was added at the Short Brothers' new works near Leysdown, where flying took place subsequently. Rolls used his glider until 10 October, achieving many long flights from the end of August, often of about 60 m (200 ft). However, having received his powered Short-Wright on 1 October, he had little further use for the glider and it was offered for sale together with its launching equipment and storage shed. It is entirely possible that Oswald Short also piloted the glider on at least one occasion before it went to the British Army. Early illustrations of the glider show it without the twin fins later added between the elevators and without the aft twin vertical rudders.

Data

Power plant: None
Wing span: 10.00 m (32 ft 10 in)
Wing area, gross: 30.19 m² (325 sq ft)
Length overall: 5.49 m (18 ft)
Range: more than 60 m (200 ft)

Variant

Glider. Single example built for Charles Rolls.

BIPLANE No 1

First flight: Probably never flown

Type: Tested as a single-seat biplane but designed as a two-seater

Notes and Structure: Although this aeroplane was exhibited at Olympia in unfinished form in March 1909, it received little publicity owing to the reluctance of Short Brothers to make information available to publishers. Indeed, the 1909 *Jane's All the World's Aircraft* carried only the following brief details and no illustration:

Body: Spruce throughout.
Wings: Continental fabric.

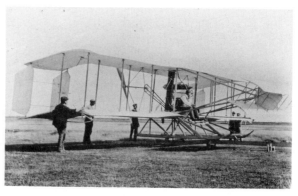

Frank McClean on the Short Biplane No 1, ready for one of his unsuccessful attempts to fly

31

Motor: 40 hp.

Propellers: Two.

Steering: Elevator forward, vertical rudder aft.

Remarks: Design embodies a number of small special features.

By the time of the 1910–11 edition of *Jane's*, the No 1 had been dropped. Designed by Horace Short and clearly influenced by the Wright biplane being flown so successfully in France at that time, it had been ordered from Short Brothers in January 1909 by Francis K. 'Frank' McClean. Construction of the airframe began in about February 1909 and within three months only part of the aircraft's Continental fabric covering and installation of an engine remained before completion.

As the write-up in the 1909 *Jane's* stated, the airframe was constructed of spruce, although the typical Wright-type landing gear skids were of ash. The biplane wings had no anhedral or dihedral and were of constant chord for most of their span, with wider chord outer sections which could be warped for control. The engine was mounted to one side of centre on the lower wing and drove two large pusher propellers. A biplane elevator incorporating a central fin was strut-mounted well ahead of the mainplanes. No tail unit as such was fitted, though four rudders were attached near the trailing edges of the wider-chord sections of the wings.

The first power plant fitted to the No 1 was a motorcar engine, which McClean found was too heavy during his first attempts to become airborne in August 1909. The following month the specified French Bariquand et Marre engine arrived at Short Brothers, being a licence-built Wright engine of 22.4 kW (30 hp).

This four cylinder engine weighed only about one-third that of the motorcar engine previously fitted to the No 1, at 96 kg (212 lb), and McClean found this much better suited to his aircraft. Like Wright aircraft of the period, No 1 was to be launched from a ground rail but on 2 and 3 November the aircraft failed to leave the ground. On 6 November a further attempt was made but as the end of the rail approached McClean used too much elevator and the aircraft finished on its back. It is unlikely that the damaged aircraft was repaired.

Data

Power plant: See NOTES

Wing span: 12.19 m (40 ft)

Wing area, gross: 53.51 m² (576 sq ft)

Length overall: 7.49 m (24 ft 7 in)

Max t/o weight: 544 kg (1,200 lb)

Variant

Biplane No 1. Single example built for Frank McClean.

BIPLANE No 2

First flight: 27 September 1909

Type: Two-seat biplane

Notes and Structure: 1909 was an epic year for powered flying in general. July alone saw Alliot Verdon Roe covering a short distance in his paper-covered triplane to become the first Briton to fly in a British aeroplane, while there was also Frenchman Louis Blériot's heroic crossing of the Channel. It was also a momentous year for Short Brothers, establishing the company as an aeroplane builder.

Moore-Brabazon lifts off in the Biplane No 2 that had been fitted with the Vivinus engine

Biplane No 2 with the Green engine installed. Here Horace Short inspects an aileron before flight

The single most important Short-built aircraft of the year was the Biplane No 2, although only one example was constructed compared to six Short-Wrights. The Biplane No 2 represented not only the first Short-built powered aeroplane to fly successfully but was of the company's own design, the latter being of great significance. However, the Biplane No 2 had been designed after work had begun on the Short-Wrights and the finished aircraft bore a number of similarities to the American design. Both types were equal-span biplanes with a single engine driving twin pusher propellers (turning the same way on the No 2 so as not to infringe a Wright patent on crossing one driving chain), and both had biplane elevators mounted forward of the wings supported wholly or partly on the skid landing gear and rear-mounted fin/fins. But major differences there were. For a start No 2's wings were of much greater span and of higher aspect ratio. The elevators were rectangular, whereas the Short-Wright used elevators with ogival tips, and No 2 used a single tall rectangular rudder aft of the elevators, unlike the Short-Wright's two small vertical surfaces between the elevators. Also No 2 used a single rear-mounted fin in place of the Short-Wright's twin rudders, while the latter's warping wing control was superseded on the No 2 by ailerons, each twin-surface aileron carried about mid-way up the outer interplane struts.

The Biplane No 2 was built to the order of J. T. C. Moore-Brabazon, a pioneer aviator who had already been associated with the balloon activities of the Short brothers and had commissioned Shorts to produce components that had gone into his unsuccessful biplane of 1907. He had learned to fly at Issy-les-Moulineaux, France, in late 1908 and indeed made his first flight of notable duration (410 m; 1,350 ft) on 4 December that year while under instruction. His mount for this flight was a Voisin biplane. The Voisin served him well and he purchased a total of three, on the last of which (Voisin No 22, later sold to A. George) he became the first Englishman to make an accredited aeroplane flight in England when, on 30 April 1909, he flew it over a distance of 137 m (450 ft) at Leysdown, Isle of Sheppey. However, about three weeks before this achievement the *Daily Mail* newspaper had announced a £1,000 prize for the first Briton to fly over a one mile course in an all-British aeroplane within the time period of one year (the first large *Daily Mail* prize), which inspired Moore-Brabazon to order the Biplane No 2 from Short Brothers.

By September the airframe of Biplane No 2 had been completed, but the 37.25–44.7 kW (50–60 hp) Green engine under manufacture by the Aster Engineering Company had still not been delivered. So as not to hold up flight testing of the aeroplane, the Belgian Vivinus engine from one of his crashed Voisins was fitted. This four-cylinder engine was of considerably lower power rating than the Green and in fact weighed considerably less at 93 kg (205 lb), compared to the Green's 119 kg (263 lb). With this Moore-Brabazon flew an impressive distance on 27 September, reportedly nearly one mile, but the aircraft was slightly damaged three days later. In repaired form the Biplane No 2 appeared with the Green engine fitted and on 30 October Moore-Brabazon won the *Daily Mail* prize. Five days later, to fulfil a bet, Moore-Brabazon flew No 2 with a piglet carried in

Who says pigs cannot fly? Not Moore-Brabazon

a basket to prove that 'pigs could fly'. Soon after, the original aft fin of No 2 was replaced by a new cruciform tail unit, in which configuration it won the British Michelin Cup. Biplane No 2 was exhibited at the March 1910 Olympia Show.

Data
Power plant: See NOTES
Wing span: 14.83 m (48 ft 8 in)
Wing area, gross: 41.81 m² (450 sq ft)
Length overall: 9.75 m (32 ft)
Max t/o weight: 674 kg (1,485 lb)
Max level speed: 39 knots (72 km/h; 45 mph)

Variant
Biplane No 2. Single aircraft ordered by J. T. C. Moore-Brabazon. Described above.

SHORT-WRIGHT MODEL A BIPLANE

First flight: 22 October 1909

Type: Two-seat biplane
Notes and Structure: By the end of 1908 only France had been chosen by Wilbur Wright as a centre for European manufacture of the Wright biplane. Despite the great enthusiasm of individual members of the Aero Club to purchase Wright biplanes after their flights as passengers earlier in the year, and the formation of British syndicates to try to win the right to construct Wright biplanes, Wilbur considered the British market too limited to warrant a speedy decision and negotiations with British syndicates were eventually broken off. Included among these was a syndicate formed by Lord Royston from members of the Aero Club, to which Eustace Short had been the advising engineer following the Aero Club's earlier decision to appoint Oswald and Eustace Short the organisation's Official Aeronautical Engineers.

In early 1909 the Wright brothers decided that it was in their best interest not to sell the patent rights to their two-seat biplane but to have examples built under sub-contract. Griffith Brewer, then the official agent for the Wrights in Britain, was asked to recommend a contractor for the biplanes and he put forward Short Brothers.

As mentioned in the Introduction, Griffith Brewer had been instrumental in finding the flying ground near Leysdown for Frank McClean and it

was here that Short Brothers established their first purpose-built workshop. Construction of the workshop had begun in February 1909, a corrugated metal building 30.48 m (100 ft) wide, 13.71 m (45 ft) deep and 7.92 m (26 ft) high with three large skylights and an opening with clear space of 12.19 m (40 ft) through which to roll out the finished aircraft. This workshop was assembled by William Harbrow, a well-established builder and contractor of iron, wood and composite churches, schools and hospitals, the blueprint for the building being dated 20 February 1909. It was opened for business in March and was thus the first purpose-built aircraft factory in Britain.

The contract to build six Wright biplanes was signed by Short Brothers in March 1909, although the intention to give Shorts the contract must have been made clear some weeks earlier as the notebook in which Horace Short made drawings of the Wright biplane at Pau in France is dated 9 February.

It was Griffith Brewer who first brought public attention to the contract, in mid-March, just days after the Leysdown works had been completed. The contract was worth £1,200 in profit for Short Brothers. It appears that the Wright brothers' assessment of the British market had been correct, for only three Short-Wrights had been committed to members of the Aero Club by the end of the month. Indeed, the last were not finally sold until the end of the year.

On 3 and 4 May respectively the Wright brothers, en route from Europe to the USA, visited Short factories at Battersea and Leysdown, commenting on the high quality of the work.

Wilbur thought the first Short-Wright could be flying by June but there was a problem. Although four airframes had been completed by Shorts by July, no engines had arrived from France. The Wright-designed engine, which developed 18.6–22.4 kW (25–30 hp), had been assigned to Leon Bollée for manufacture. This was a fairly ordinary four-cylinder vertical engine of two-cycle type. The cylinders, which were made separately and fitted with water jackets, were mounted on a built-up crankcase made of aluminium. All the valves were in the cylinder heads and the valve gearing was of the usual type. The engine had a free exhaust and auxiliary exhaust ports were provided at the end of the cylinders. The one special feature of this engine was that there was no carburettor, the fuel being forced directly through a mixing valve into the cylinders by a pump worked by worm gear from the crankshaft. From the same shaft was driven also the oil pump for lubrication and the base of the crankcase formed an oil reservoir from which the oil was pumped up to the oil circulation system. Ignition was by high tension magneto. A small rotary pump was used to circulate the cooling water and the radiator consisted of a number of flattened brass tubes connected at the top and bottom into suitable healers. In the event,

Charles Rolls flying the first Short-Wright Model A on 21 December 1909

Short Brothers probably received only two engines from Leon Bollée, in September, although some sources state that he supplied four, the remainder coming from the better remembered French supplier Bariquand et Marre. Each engine weighed 99 kg (218 lb).

Deliveries of Short-Wrights began from 1 October 1909, starting with No 1 for Charles Rolls, who had been the most enthusiastic Aero Club supporter of the Wrights. Details of these six aircraft, their purchasers and their achievements can be found under Variants. In original form the Short-Wright was an equal-span biplane with wire-braced unstaggered two-spar wings without dihedral. Most of the span was constant chord, although the trailing-edges of the wings curved towards the tips of the warping sections. The warping sections for lateral control comprised the two outermost bays. Nine pairs of interplane struts were used, exactly as on the original Wright *Flyer*, and these formed eight bays. The starboard inner bay carried the engine and the corresponding port bay the two side-by-side seats for the pilot and passenger. The landing gear comprised two long skids, braced to both sets of wings. Take-off was from a trolley and launching rail, as no wheels were provided. Control was by the warping wings, a biplane elevator carried above the front of the skids and braced to the lower wing, and rear-

mounted and boom-supported twin vertical rudders. As for the original *Flyer*, the engine drove two pusher propellers via chains, the port chain being crossed to reverse the direction of propeller rotation.

Data

Power plant: See NOTES
Wing span: 12.49 m (41 ft)
Wing area, gross: 47.85 m² (515 sq ft)
Length overall: 8.84 m (29 ft)
Weight empty: approx 363 kg (800 lb)
T/o weight (pilot only): 476 kg (1,050 lb)
Max t/o weight (pilot and passenger): 540 kg (1,190 lb)
Max level speed: 43 knots (80 km/h; 50 mph)
Normal maximum speed: 35 knots (64 km/h; 40 mph)
Endurance
   (pilot only): 2 h 20 min
   (pilot and passenger): 1 h 35 min

Variants

No 1. Delivered to Charles Rolls on 1 October 1909 with Bollée engine. After a number of 'hops' beginning 22 October, the last ending in minor damage to the biplane, Rolls flew 2.4 km (1½ miles) on 1 November, so winning the first of the Aero Club's £25 prizes for a flight of more than 250 yds. On the next day he won the £105 prize money and Solomon Cup for a half mile return flight. On 4 November he was again in the money, winning an Aero Club £50 prize for a flight of one mile at the Aero Club's flying ground, during which he attained an altitude of 18 m (60 ft), the greatest height seen at Shellbeach up to that time. In December Rolls managed a 24 km (15 mile) cross-country flight and on 1 January 1910 No 1 became the first Short-Wright to carry a passenger (Cecil Grace). In 1910 Major Sir Alexander Bannerman took over the Balloon Company of the Royal Engineers, British Army; the very first heavier-than-air aircraft operated by the Aeroplane branch based at Salisbury Plain was the No 1, which has variously been quoted as having been presented to the War Office by Rolls or sold to it for £1,000. The latter seems more likely on the basis of Rolls' other business commitments and his purchase of a French Wright. Whatever the case, No 1 was sent by road to Farnborough in April, after being exhibited at Olympia, and in the following months Rolls began instructing officers in its use. The No 1 remained the Company's only aeroplane until the arrival of the French Farman-Paulhan biplane. The Wright biplane that made the first double crossing of the English Channel on 2 June 1910 (from which a letter was dropped to the Aéro Club de France), and the machine he flew

McClean's Short-Wright No 3 with a tailplane behind the rudders and a wheeled landing gear

at the Wolverhampton and Bournemouth aviation meetings (where he was killed on 12 July), was a French Wright built by Astra Cie.

No 2. Delivered to Alec Ogilvie in October 1909 and first flown with a Bollée engine on 3 November. Like Rolls' French Astra-Wright, No 2 was flown at the June 1910 Wolverhampton meeting, then at Bournemouth, and in August at Lanark, his speciality being slow-speed flying. In 1910 No 2 was fitted with wheels.

No 3. Delivered to Frank McClean on 16 October 1909 without an engine. McClean hoped to achieve flight while awaiting a Bariquand et Marre engine by adopting for the second time the power plant from his motorcar. This was not successful and the aeroplane was returned to Shorts, from where it was redelivered in the following month with the French B & M installed. Fitted with a tailplane behind the rudders in May 1910 and wheels.

No 4. Delivered on 26 November 1909 to Maurice Egerton. He first flew No 4 on 1 December. Re-engined with a 37.25–44.7 kW (50–60 hp) Green in early 1911.

No 5. Delivered on 11 January 1910 to Percy Grace. First flown by Cecil Grace on 14 February 1910. Subsequently given a tailplane behind the rudders.

No 6. Ordered by Ernest Pitman but purchased by, and delivered to, Charles Rolls as his third Wright type (two British, one French) on 23 March 1910. This was the first Short-Wright to feature a tailplane and on 24 March was flown 42 km (26 miles). Subsequently it was disassembled to be married to Short No 3 Biplane components as the Power Glider (see No 3 Biplane entry). Never completed in this new form, the components were retrieved by Shorts. No 6 was sold then to Alec Ogilvie. It later flew in new and much modified form with the front elevators removed and replaced by a monoplane elevator to the rear of the vertical tail, a new landing gear incorporating two triangular fins forward, and other changes. With a 37.25 kW (50 hp) NEC engine fitted weighing almost the same as the less-powerful Wright, at 100 kg (220 lb), it flew

228 km (142 miles) in December 1910 as his bid to win the Michelin Cup. In 1911, with a new nacelle fitted to give the crew some measure of comfort and protection against the weather, No 6 flew with four persons on board. This aircraft was almost certainly the last to survive, being in fully service-able condition in the summer of 1914.

BIPLANE No 3

First flight: Not flown

Type: Single-seat biplane
Notes and Structure: This, the third Short Brothers' powered biplane of original design, was built for Charles Rolls. Work on its design began in

Biplane No 3

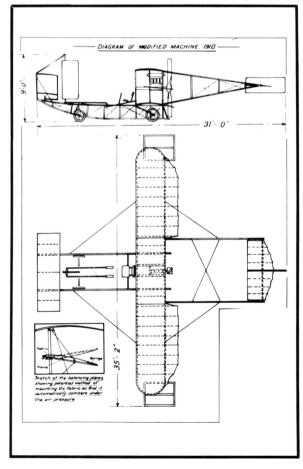

the latter part of 1909 and was clearly intended to be a smaller and lighter version of the successful Biplane No 2 but incorporating several improve-ments. Perhaps the main innovation was the inclu-sion of four wheels on the landing gear, allowing the aircraft to dispense with the launch rail but so arranged that they retracted via springs after take-off to permit a skid landing. The new tail unit comprised a fixed tailplane and rectangular fin, and new ailerons of rectangular form were fitted. These ailerons or 'balancers' were skinned with fabric produced by the British Rubber Company (as were the other surfaces) in a patented method of spring-torsioned covering so that it automati-cally cambered under air pressure. The forward rudder was also of revised form and power was entrusted to a four-cylinder 26 kW (35 hp) Green engine weighing 72 kg (158 lb), driving a single pusher propeller.

The Biplane No 3 attracted five further orders and was exhibited at the 1910 Olympia Show, where No 2 also appeared. However, Rolls was unsuccessful in his attempts to get No 3 airborne and all further machines of the type were cancel-led. After this disappointment Rolls removed the lattice girder-type chassis and engine and married these to his second Short-Wright Model A (No 6) which he had taken delivery of on 23 March that year. Unfortunately this hybrid was not yet completed when Rolls was killed during the Bournemouth Aviation Week.

Data
Power plant: See NOTES
Wing span: 10.72 m (35 ft 2 in)
Wing area, gross: 26.20 m² (282 sq ft)
Length overall: 9.45 m (31 ft)
Height overall: 2.74 m (9 ft)
Weight empty: 298 kg (657 lb)
Max t/o weight: 390 kg (860 lb)
Max level speed (estimated): 43 knots (80 km/h; 50 mph)

Variant
Biplane No 3. Single example built for Charles Rolls. Described above.

Additional notes:
The following details of the Biplane No 3 are listed as this aircraft has rarely been fully described.

Wing chord: 1.52 m (5 ft)
Wing aspect ratio: 6.0
Interplane gap: 1.32 m (4 ft 4 in)
Tailplane area: 2.00 m² (21.5 sq ft)
Fin area: 0.93 m² (10 sq ft)
Elevator area: 5.11 m² (55 sq ft)
Rudder area: 0.93 m² (10 sq ft)
Propeller diameter: 2.29 m (7 ft 6 in)

DUNNE II and V

First flights: (Dunne II and V) June 1910

Type: single-seat tailless biplanes
Notes and Structure: Briton Lieut (later Captain) J. W. Dunne earned his place in aviation history as the man who originated the tailless powered aircraft. Such was the inherent stability of developed Dunne aircraft that they could be flown 'hands off'.

In 1906 Lieut Dunne conducted secret experiments for the British Army into tailless aeroplanes, having already patented a monoplane design. The Dunne I was constructed at the Farnborough Balloon Factory in 1906 and in the following year was tested at the Duke of Atholl's estate in Scotland. This aircraft did not fly owing to an accident on the launching apparatus. In 1909 Short Brothers was requested to construct the Dunne II, an unusual triplane designed by Dunne in 1906 but assigned to Prof Huntingdon by permission of the War Office. An accompanying illustration shows the configuration of this machine, which achieved one or two brief flights at Eastchurch in 1910, and in 1912–13 flew well in modified form.

The Dunne III, which Shorts had no hand in, was a glider of 1908, successfully flown by Lieut D. L. Gibbs at the Duke of Atholl's estate, achieving stable glides in very high winds. The Dunne IV was a powered swept-wing tailless aircraft, basically a larger Dunne III but with a REP engine. It was flown briefly on several occasions in Scotland during July 1908 in the hands of Lieut Gibbs, some 'flights' covering about 45 m (150 ft).

Early in 1910 the War Office abandoned its experiments with Dunne aircraft. As a result, the Blair Atholl Aeroplane Syndicate was formed and the Dunne V was ordered from Short Brothers. Powered by a 37.25–44.7 kW (50–60 hp) Green engine driving two pusher propellers, it first flew in June 1910. It was a biplane with swept-back parallel-chord wings without stagger. The wing camber varied throughout, although the maximum camber was towards the tips and the minimum at

Prof Huntingdon's Dunne II, otherwise known as the Huntingdon Monoplane

Dunne V biplane built by Short Brothers for the Blair Atholl Aeroplane Syndicate

the inboard sections. A short nacelle formed the fuselage for the pilot only, with the engine installed to his rear. The undercarriage comprised a twin wheel main assembly and a single smaller wheel and skid, with a skid to protect the wings under each tip. Interplane curtain-type rudders were provided at the wingtips and wing ailerons for control. Although the Dunne V proved automatically stable in flight, it turned out to be considerably heavier than expected at design stage.

Short Brothers also made important component contributions to the Dunne D 6, D 7 and D 8, the D 6 being a monoplane of 1906 design (originally offered to the War Office and built for Col Capper in 1910). The D 7 was a 37.25 kW (50 hp) Gnome-engined single-seat monoplane capable of 52 knots (96 km/h: 60 mph) and was followed by the similar two-seat D 7*bis* with a 52 kW (70 hp) Gnome engine. The D 8 was very similar to the Dunne V but with the 37.25–44.7 kW (50–60 hp)

Green engine driving a single propeller. This biplane proved capable of only 39 knots (72 km/h; 45 mph). These components were ordered by the Blair Atholl Aeroplane Syndicate. Other Dunne aircraft followed but did not involve work for Short Brothers.

Data *(Dunne V)*
Power plant: see NOTES
Wing span: 14.02 m (46 ft)
Wing area, gross: 48.96 m² (527 sq ft)
Length of fuselage nacelle: 5.48 m (18 ft)
Max t/o weight: 703 kg (1,550 lb)

Variants
Dunne II. Unusual triplane of 1906 design, built for Prof Huntingdon in 1910. Modified in 1912.
Dunne V. Successful biplane built for the Blair Atholl Aeroplane Syndicate.

S.27 TYPE (Short manufacture numbers S.26–S.35, S.38, S.43–S.44)

First flight: mid-1910

Type: Two-seat pusher biplanes
Notes and Structure: Even as construction of the final Short-Wright was taking place, several of the best known aviators at the Aero Club were of the opinion that the American design had been surpassed by aircraft flying in France. There was evidence to support this. At the world's first international aviation meeting, held in Reims between 22 and 29 August 1909, of the twenty-three aircraft that flew, three were Wright types while three were Antoinettes, three Blériots, three Henry Farmans and no fewer than seven Voisins. At this meeting, an Antoinette established the first speed record over 100 km, while Henry Farman in one of his own types set world duration and distance records. Also at Reims Louis Blériot set a new world speed record, which lasted until April of the following year. Only French aircraft held the record thereafter until the outbreak of the First World War.

Henry Farman was the biggest money winner at Reims and it was generally accepted that his pusher biplane configuration held the greatest potential of any aircraft then flying. Even Charles Rolls had to admit that the Wright biplane was

outdated; he had been one of Europe's greatest exponents of the American type and had purchased British- and French-built examples. One of the main factors of Farman's success lay in the selection of a Gnome rotary engine to power his aircraft, developed by the French Séguin brothers from 1907 and which first appeared in 1908 as a seven-cylinder engine weighing 75 kg (165 lb) and giving a rating of 37.25 kW (50 hp).

Another aviator flying in France that saw great promise in the Farman type was Roger Sommer, who had designed his own aircraft in 1908 (which proved unsuccessful) and had then purchased a Farman, setting records and racing at Reims.

S.27 built for Cecil Grace with Sommer-type tail unit

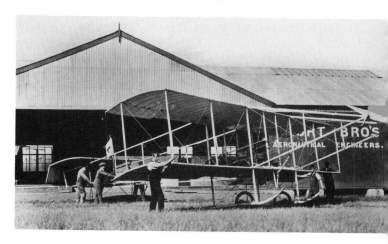

S.28 rebuilt to S.35 standard, except for the aileron arrangement and the use of twin tail skids

Towards the end of 1909 Sommer began producing his own pusher biplane aircraft, heavily based on the Farman type but incorporating his own innovations. The latter included the use of a single tailplane with elevator and upper and lower rudders (one example had twin rudders under the tailplane, but this was not standard), and very wide chord upper wing ailerons instead of the neat inset rectangular upper and lower ailerons to be found on the Farman.

At the new Eastchurch factory, Horace Short decided not to take up an option to construct further Short-Wrights but designed a pusher biplane of his own. This had Farman-type wings with upper and lower ailerons, a forward elevator of Farman type but a modified Sommer-type monoplane tail unit and Sommer under-tail arched skids. Horace was familiar with the Sommer biplane, as Rolls had already purchased an example which had flown at Eastchurch. This Short design began a series of highly successful pusher biplanes that were used for event flying and instruction, the early examples accommodating the pilot forward and the passenger/pupil to his rear. Although the first such aircraft was S.26, the series was generally known as the S.27 type, followed by

improved models which made military history. All aircraft of the so-called S.27 type are listed under VARIANTS.

Data
Power plant: See VARIANTS
Wing span: *(S.26, S.27 and S.28)* 10.41 m (34 ft 2 in); *(S.29, S.32, S.33, S.34, S.35, S.38, S.43 and S.44)* 14.15 m (46 ft 5 in)
Wing area: *(S.26, S.27 and S.28)* 44.59 m² (480 sq ft); *(S.29 etc)* 48.03 m² (517 sq ft)
Length overall: *(S.26, S.27 and S.28)* 12.34 m (40 ft 6 in); *(S.29 etc)* 12.83 m (42 ft 1 in)
Height overall: *(S.29 etc with upper and lower rudders)* 3.66 m (12 ft)
Weight empty: *(S.26, S.27 and S.28)* 454 kg (1,000 lb); *(S.29 etc)* 499 kg (1,100 lb)
Max t/o weight: *(S.26, S.27 and S.28)* 635 kg (1,400 lb); *(S.29 etc)* 699 kg (1,540 lb)
Max level speed: *(S.26, S.27 and S.28)* 35 knots (64 km/h; 40 mph); *(S.29 etc with 50 hp Gnome)* 34 knots (63 km/h; 39 mph); *(S.32, S.33, S.34 and S.38 with 70 hp Gnome)* 42 knots (77 km/h; 48 mph)
Stalling speed: *(S.29 etc with 50 hp Gnome)* 29 knots (55 km/h; 34 mph); *(S.32 etc with 70 hp Gnome)* 33 knots (61 km/h; 38 mph)
Endurance: *(S.32 etc: A with 50 hp Gnome, B with 70 hp Gnome)* A 4 h, B 5 h

Variants
S.26. First of four original S.27 series aircraft with 30 kW (40 hp) Green engine, built for Frank McClean as No 3 in his private fleet of aeroplanes. Featured tailplane and elevator above single rudder. Often flown by George C. Colmore (pilot certificate No 15). Original engine replaced with 37.25 kW (50 hp) Gnome rotary and modifications made to forward elevator and tailplane in summer of 1910. Used as an instruction aircraft for Navy pilots during 1911 but was the least successful machine.
S.27. Similar to S.26 for Cecil Grace (pilot certificate No 4) but with a 44.7 kW (60 hp) ENV eight-cylinder Vee engine weighing 130 kg (287 lb) and Sommer-type tail unit with upper and lower rudders. Flown during the Wolverhampton and Bournemouth Aviation Weeks in June and July 1910. Acquired by Frank McClean after Grace died in a flying accident, as his No 7. Later converted into the Tandem Twin (McClean No 11).
S.28. Similar to S.26, for J. T. C. Moore-Brabazon. Subsequently purchased by McClean as his No 5 after Moore-Brabazon gave up flying. Fitted with a 37.25 kW (50 hp) Gnome rotary engine from November 1910, then 37.25–44.7 kW (50–60 hp) Green for an attempt to win the £4,000 Baron de

S.32, the second of the improved S.27 series, in use as a trainer for Territorials in 1911

Forest prize for the longest distance flown in a straight line into Europe by a British pilot flying an all-British aeroplane during the year 1910. Not used for the attempt (which was won by T. O. M. Sopwith with a flight of 154 nm [285 km; 177 miles] on 18 December from Eastchurch to Beaumont, Belgium). Used between March and August 1911 as instruction aircraft for Navy pilots, first being used to teach the later-famed Lieut Charles Rumney Samson to fly. At end of 1911 S.28 emerged with S.35-type extended wings and crew nacelle. Finally was taken over by Navy as military No 66, without forward elevator, known as the Eastchurch 'Gun Machine' and used for gun (nose-mounted Maxim) and bombing experiments.

S.29. Last of the original four S.27 types. Intended to be similar to S.27 but given extended upper wings. The lower wing ailerons were deleted and a central tail skid replaced the usual type to Cecil Grace order. This aircraft can be viewed as the first of the improved S.27 types. Used by Grace to establish his bid for Baron de Forest prize but was lost with its pilot on the return flight from France, despite the carriage of Horace Short-designed flotation bags in case of accident.

S.32. Second actual improved S.27 type, incorporating S.29's modifications (except with upper and lower ailerons) but with side-by-side seating and dual controls as Short's first purpose-designed trainer. 52 kW (70 hp) Gnome rotary engine. Built for Frank McClean as his No 8 and first flown in July 1911. Used to give flying instruction to members of the Territorials during winter of 1911–12. In 1913 McClean chose S.32 for modification to suit an anticipated expedition up the river Nile (see S.80). Apart from modifications to provide a crew nacelle and twin tail skids, its wings were extended, giving an upper span of 21.49 m (70 ft 6 in). The outer upper tapering wing panels had slight dihedral. In this form it re-emerged in May 1913 as McClean's No 14 but was clearly unsuited to the task and was not used. It was one of

two aircraft presented simultaneously to the RNAS shortly before the war, becoming military 904 and fitted later with shorter-span wings.

S.33. Similar to S.32 and purchased by Frank McClean. Used with S.32 to instruct Territorials. Subsequently converted into a seaplane. In this form, on 10 August 1912, McClean left Harty Ferry, Isle of Sheppey, and flew between the upper and lower spans of Tower Bridge and then flew on to underfly all the other bridges to Westminster, where he landed. The police instructed him to taxi back to Shadwell Basin before mooring. Having taken off again, S.33 side-slipped and a float struck a barge. It was dismantled at Shadwell Dock and taken to Eastchurch by road.

S.34. Built for McClean as a training aircraft; fleet No 6. Used with S.28. First of improved S.27 type, flying before S.32 and S.33. Later given increased fuel tankage for long-duration flights. Became first RNAS aircraft (serial 1) and later modified, including adoption of tandem crew nacelle. On 17 August 1911 Lieut Gerrard had set a world passenger-carrying record on S.34 of 4 h 13 min. Later given four-wheel main undercarriage.

S.35. Basically improved S.27 type but with the first use of a tandem crew nacelle to Maurice Egerton's order. Upper ailerons only and 37.25 kW (50 hp) Gnome rotary engine.

S.38. First flown in May 1911 as trainer to replace the S.26. Became famous on 10 January 1912, when Samson flew it from a platform on board HMS *Africa*, a 15,740-ton battleship at anchor. This was the first time a British pilot had flown from a ship. Samson repeated the take-off on 9 May, but this time from the 15,785-ton HMS

Frank McClean navigates between the spans of Tower Bridge on 10 August 1912, to the delight of the Press

S.38 at the May 1912 Naval Review on board HMS *Hibernia*. In front of S.38 on *Hibernia*'s over-turret platform is S.41, which was flown as a seaplane from water by Samson and Longmore but not from the platform

Samson rises from *Hibernia* on 9 May 1912

Hibernia that had been fitted with *Africa*'s platform. *Hibernia*, taking part in a Naval Review off Portland, was steaming at 10½ knots at the time, making this the first ever take-off from a moving ship (something by then not even achieved by the American Eugene B. Ely, the first man to fly an aeroplane from a ship). However, it has been said that Samson made a secret flight from *Africa* as early as December 1911, while the vessel was in Sheerness Harbour. For these experiments, S.38 was fitted with flotation bags. S.38 was badly damaged on 9 July 1912 while being lifted on board the 14,420-ton battleship HMS *London*, the third Royal Navy vessel to be experimentally fitted with a flying platform. It reappeared at the end of

August in modified form, with a 15.85 m (52 ft) wing span, and the twin under-tailplane rudders and long crew nacelle of the types then being fitted to S.34, plus other revisions; a 52 kW (70 hp) Gnome engine had replaced the 37.25 kW (50 hp) Gnome sometime after the *Africa* flight. S.38 was the Navy's second aircraft and as such carried the military serial 2. Later given four-wheel main undercarriage.

S.43 and S.44. On 19 June 1912 the Central Flying School of the RFC was established at Upavon. These trainers were delivered to the CFS during the following month, receiving military serials 401 and 402.

Having achieved the first-ever take-off in an aeroplane from a moving ship and thereafter landed successfully at Lodmoor, Samson had every right to look pleased

S.39 TRIPLE TWIN

First flight: 18 September 1911

Type: Two-seat, twin-engined biplane

Notes and Structure: Short Brothers can justly claim several of aviation history's important 'firsts', not least of which recognises the company as the first to put an aircraft into series production. However, over the years several spurious 'firsts' have also been credited to the company by others, which have included the claims that Short Brothers was the first aircraft company (in fact the French Voisin brothers company was established in 1905), that it originated the first twin-engined aircraft, and that its Sperrin was Britain's first four-jet bomber. The second of these mentioned is most obviously incorrect, as among aircraft with twin engines flown before any by Short Brothers include those of Hiram Maxim, Russian Alexander Mozhaiski and Frenchman Clément Ader in the nineteenth century. Short Brothers was not even first to construct an aeroplane with two petrol engines.

The first twin-engined aircraft of Short design was the S.39, known widely as the Triple Twin. Its construction followed the granting to the brothers in 1911 of patents covering multi-engine arrangements. Based on the S.27, it had braced biplane wings of parallel chord and initially equal span. Ailerons were fitted to upper and lower wings. A forward elevator was mounted on outriggers. The fuselage nacelle accommodated two persons side-by-side with dual controls and was attached to the lower wing. The two 37.25 kW (50 hp) Gnome rotary engines were installed in tandem in the nose and tail of the nacelle, the forward engine ahead of the cockpit driving two tractor propellers and the rear-mounted engine driving a single pusher propeller. Driving chains of Renold type were used to connect the forward engine to the tractor propellers, the port chain being crossed to allow counter-rotation. The tandem engines themselves rotated in opposite directions. The tail unit comprised a tailplane with three rudders below.

One innovation of the design was that either engine could be throttled back or shut down without loss of control and therefore the S.39 can rightly be claimed as the first aircraft to use twin engines as a way of increasing safety. The Triple Twin was first flown by Frank McClean on 18 September 1911, adding this to his growing personal fleet of aircraft as No 10. This first flight was followed by circuits of the Eastchurch airfield with Commander Charles Samson as passenger, during which the engines were throttled back in turn. The Triple Twin was also one of McClean's aircraft loaned to the Admiralty, eventually becoming

S.39 Triple Twin in original configuration with equal-span wings and two fuel tanks

number 3 under the November 1912 military numbering system. In 1913 the S.39 was taken back to Short Brothers for modification (see Variant).

Data

Power plant: See NOTES
Wing span (standard): 10.36 m (34 ft)
Wing span (extended, upper and lower): 15.24 m (50 ft)
Wing span (second extension to upper only): 19.51 m (64 ft)
Wing area, gross: 40.4–46.45 m² (435–500 sq ft)
Length overall: 13.71 m (45 ft)
Height overall: 3.66 m (12 ft)
Tailplane span: 3.96 m (13 ft)
Weight empty: 816 kg (1,800 lb)
Max t/o weight: 953 kg (2,100 lb)
Speed: 30–48 knots (56–89 km/h; 35–55 mph)

Variant

S.39 Triple Twin. Single example for Frank McClean (see also Maurice Egerton's S.35). Original equal-span wings were subsequently fitted in turn with upper wing extensions, upper and lower wing extensions, and finally extensions to the already equally extended wings. Diameter of each propeller was 2.6 m (8 ft 6 in). In early 1913 it was taken back by Short Brothers and reappeared in July as a totally different aircraft. A new fuselage nacelle for two persons seated in tandem with individual cockpits replaced the old, whilst only a single 60 kW (80 hp) Gnome pusher engine and propeller remained. The unequal-span wings used a new aerofoil section and no front elevator was fitted to the aircraft. More rounded rudders replaced the original triple type and the undercarriage used two main wheel units. Capable of a maximum speed of 56 knots (105 km/h; 65 mph), it was used as a trainer until the First World War broke out, thereafter going to France as a communications aircraft with Samson's Eastchurch Squadron.

43

(S.27) TANDEM TWIN

First flight: 29 October 1911

Type: Two-seat, twin-engined biplane

Notes and Structure: Having observed the Triple Twin, Horace Short decided to test a similar engine layout but with the forward engine directly driving a tractor propeller. The chosen aircraft for modification was the S.27 originally owned by Cecil Grace but acquired by Frank McClean as number 7 in his private fleet.

The modification from S.27 type to Tandem Twin was basic, with the new tractor engine and propeller fitted forward of a fuselage nacelle, two fuel tanks placed between the wings instead of the previous one, the addition of two extra rudders above the tailplane and a strengthened undercarriage. In tests the Tandem Twin was successfully flown with each engine in turn throttled back but proved unstable. However, in this new form it became No 11 in McClean's fleet and was tested with the Triple Twin's upper wing extensions. Like McClean's S.39, the Tandem Twin was loaned to the Admiralty as a trainer.

Data

Power plant: Two 37.25 kW (50 hp) Gnome rotary engines.
Wing span (original): 10.41 m (34 ft 2 in)
Wing area, gross: 44.59 m² (480 sq ft)
Length overall: 12.34 m (40 ft 6 in)
Max level speed: 48 knots (89 km/h; 55 mph)

Variant

(S.27) Tandem Twin. Single example only, as described in NOTES. Also known as the *Gnome Sandwich* because of its engine layout. Wrecked in a flying accident.

A posed photograph of McClean in the cockpit of the Tandem Twin in 1911

TRACTOR BIPLANES (Short manufacture numbers S.36, S.41, S.45, S.47, S.48, S.49, S.50, S.51 and S.52)

First flight: (S.36) 10 January 1912

Type: Single- or two-seat tractor biplanes

Notes and Structure: The importance of Frank McClean's seemingly boundless generosity in loaning his private aircraft to the Admiralty cannot be overstated. It was due to McClean that Navy officers first took to the air as pilots and it was upon his aircraft that British naval aviation was founded. Equally important, it was McClean's purchase of the first Short tractor biplane that introduced this type of aircraft into Navy service, although the actual aircraft (S.36) was on loan only. This was, therefore, the forerunner of the famous Short seaplanes of the First World War.

In 1911 Horace Short designed a tractor biplane, which interested McClean sufficiently to gain an order for a single example. Like all Short aircraft, it had been carefully conceived, relying partly on lessons learned from those pusher biplanes then flying and partly on Horace's skill as an innovator. Numbered S.36, it was an unequal-span

S.36 as originally flown, with partially covered fuselage

biplane with upper ailerons only. The tapering fuselage, covered only from the engine cowling to the rear of the tandem cockpits, was mounted mid-way between the wings and carried a flat tailplane with elevator and an aft balanced rudder. Power was provided by a 52 kW (70 hp) Gnome rotary engine. First flown in early 1912, it was loaned to the Naval Flying School at Eastchurch. It was upon this aircraft that the Navy gained valuable flying experience with tractor biplanes. Subsequently the fuselage was fully covered to improve directional stability and later still the lower wing was raised to match those of follow-on tractor aircraft from Shorts.

As a result of flying the S.36, two similar aircraft were ordered for Navy service but with interchangeable wheel and float landing gears. The first to appear was S.41 with a 74.5 kW (100 hp) Gnome engine, a reduced gap between the lower wing and the covered fuselage, and twin floats supplemented by stabilising airbags under the tail and wingtips. First flown as a landplane in April 1912, it was taken as a seaplane (with S.38) to the Naval Review off Portland on board HMS *Hibernia* in May 1912 but had to be lowered into the water for take-off. By the time of the July Review off Portsmouth, a military numbering system had been introduced and S.41 became H10, later simply 10. In September it was flown as a landplane during Army manoeuvres, in the company of S.45 and S.47, returning to seaplane configuration thereafter and serving for a brief time, with S.45, as a coastal patrol aircraft in Scotland. In late 1913 it was used in the development of mechanically folding wings and for this it again reverted to landplane form. In addition to the wings, the tail unit was of revised configuration. S.41 ended its career with a 104.5 kW (140 hp) engine and was used in the Dardanelles campaign of 1915.

S.45, mentioned above, was the second aircraft ordered as a result of flying S.36. It had a reduced wing span and a 52 kW (70 hp) Gnome engine and first flew in May 1912 as a landplane. As it was a landplane at the time of the adoption of the military numbering system, S.45 first became T5 (Trac-

The original S.41 with military serial 10 on its tail, flown by Commander Samson at the Carlingnose naval station in Scotland in October 1912. The insert shows Samson in flight in S.41 during the May 1912 Naval Review

Commander Samson in Flight.   May 1912

tor 5) and then simply 5 (H for hydro-aeroplane was not adopted for this aircraft). It was flown as a seaplane during the Naval Review off Portsmouth in 1912 and took part in Army manoeuvres that year as a landplane, thereafter readopting its seaplane form which comprised a single main pontoon and mid-span and under-tail stabilising floats. It was lost during service in Scotland.

Information on other aircraft in this series can be found under VARIANTS. However, one other is worthy of mention here. On 24 July 1912 McClean flew S.47, which became known as the Triple Tractor. This had the longest fuselage of any aircraft in the series, to make room for two 37.25 kW (50 hp) Gnome engines in tandem within the forward fuselage. The forward engine directly drove a tractor propeller, while the aft engine powered two propellers carried at mid-span on the forward interplane struts, via chains. These counter-rotated as on the Short-Wrights but were tractor propellers. Two seats were provided (for the pilot and passenger) in typical 'sociable' layout. S.47 was purchased from Shorts by the Navy (becoming T4) and was flown during Army manoeuvres in September that year. Thereafter it was used for experimental work.

The original S.45 with central main pontoon and mid-span stabilising floats. The military serial 5 is just visible on the tail

Data

Power plant: See NOTES and VARIANTS
Wing span: *(S.36)* 14.15 m (46 ft 5 in); *(S.41 types)* 15.24 m (50 ft); *(S.45 types)* 12.80 m (42 ft); *(S.47)* 14.63 m (48 ft)
Wing area, gross: *(S.36)* 47.85 m² (515 sq ft); *(S.41 types and S.45 types)* 41.81 m² (450 sq ft); *(S.47)* 46.45 m² (500 sq ft)
Length overall: *(S.36 and S.45 types)* 10.82 m (35 ft 6 in); *(S.41 types, seaplane form)* 11.89 m (39 ft); *(S.47)* 12.50 m (41 ft)
Height overall: *(S.41 types)* 3.58 m (11 ft 9 in) from top of floats; *(S.45 types)* 4.88 m (16 ft)
Weight empty: *(S.36)* 386 kg (850 lb); *(S.41)* 499 kg (1,100 lb); *(S.45 types)* 490 kg (1,080 lb)
Max t/o weight: *(S.36)* 590 kg (1,300 lb); *(S.41 types)* 726 kg (1,600 lb); *(S.45 types)* 680 kg (1,500 lb)
Max level speed: *(S.36 only)* 50 knots (93 km/h; 58 mph); (others) 52 knots (97 km/h; 60 mph)
Endurance: 5 h

Close-up of the S.47 Triple Tractor, showing the crossed chain arrangement for the outer propeller to achieve contra rotation

S.51 (modified S.41 type) with military serial 20.

Variants

S.36. Original tractor biplane for McClean, as described above.
S.41. First Short tractor biplane for Naval Wing of RFC, with 74.5 kW (100 hp) Gnome engine.
S.45. Second Short tractor biplane for Naval Wing of RFC, with 52 kW (70 hp) Gnome engine. Later modified to include ailerons with both up and down movement and raised decking in tandem cockpit area.
S.47. Triple Tractor, with two 37.25 kW (50 hp) Gnome engines driving three propellers.
S.48, S.49 and S.50. Similar aircraft to S.45 in final modified form, supplied as landplane trainers to CFS between October 1912 and February 1913. Airframes handed over to Admiralty at start of First World War, being installed with 74.5 kW (100 hp) Clerget engines and carrying new military serials 1268 and 1279.
S.51 and S.52. Two S.41 types ordered for RNAS as 74.5 kW (100 hp) Gnome-engined seaplanes, with improved wing sections, no diagonal interplane bracing struts at wingtips and other changes. Became Navy 20 and 21. Aircraft 20 used in experiments with Gregory-Riley-White wheel/float undercarriage, as was S.61 (which see).

MONOPLANE

First flight: 24 February 1912

Type: Single-seat monoplane

Notes and Structure: Several early Short Brothers aircraft had strong Royal Navy connections, originally because of the generosity of Frank McClean who made machines from his considerable private collection available to the Admiralty. At first McClean's aircraft were loaned unofficially but from 6 December 1910 authority was given in General Fleet Orders. In this manner the Senior Service began flying. When an official numbering system came into use for military aircraft, the lettering system H for hydro-aeroplane, M for monoplane and T for tractor was used. This system was still in use during the 1912 Naval Reviews but was superseded by a straight numbering system from November of that year, with the Royal Navy being allocated numbers 1 to 200. Interestingly, numbers 1 to 5 were all Short aircraft.

One of McClean's aircraft flown by Navy pilots at the Naval Flying School from November 1911 was a monoplane built by the Universal Aviation Company and known as the *Birdling*. One very enthusiastic pilot was Charles Rumney Samson. Horace Short was not slow to appreciate this and set about designing a monoplane, which was constructed during January and February 1912. Luckily Short Brothers had experience in the construction of monoplanes prior to this, having carried out extensive work on *Birdling* for McClean after its initial purchase.

Not altogether surprisingly, the Short monoplane had many similarities to the highly successful French Blériot XI but benefited from the company's growing design and constructional experience and predilection for very sturdy airframes. This monoplane, which had no name, had shoulder-mounted constant-chord wings with rounded tips that were braced by eight wires to a steel cabane structure above the engine and wire braced below. The 37.25 kW (50 hp) Gnome engine was level with the leading-edge of the wings and, because of its overhung mounting, it was without support between the crankcase and Cheuvière-type propeller. The main wheels of the landing gear were carried on a very strong chassis of ash and small skids were incorporated of the type prevalent in aircraft exhibited at the Aero Show in Paris; the skids would have been of little use in the event of failure of the wheels. A long universally jointed tailskid was employed to allow plenty of ground clearance for the downwards cambered rectangular underfuselage-mounted tailplane and elevator, whilst a balanced rudder was fitted. Typical for this type of monoplane was the use of wing warping for control.

Having made its maiden flight in early 1912, the Short monoplane was given the military serial number M.2 and was flown by Samson. It was assigned to be flown during a 1912 Naval Review and indeed Samson flew the aircraft before making his historic flight from HMS *Hibernia* in Short S.38, but some damage was sustained by the

The Monoplane in earliest form. Note the tailskid has rubber bungee shock absorption

monoplane on 6 May in a landing incident. By the time of this flight the rear fuselage structure had also been fabric covered to match the forward section. After repair by Short Brothers, the monoplane was flown by other Navy pilots and from November was renumbered under the new military aircraft system which coincided with the founding of the Air Department of the Admiralty. It has been suggested that No 14 was the monoplane's military serial and this might indeed have been the case, although a Bristol-built Coanda-type seaplane reportedly also carried 14. According to the 1913 *Jane's*, the monoplane was still in existence that year but it is unlikely to have served beyond 1913.

MONOPLANE No 2

First flight: 21 October 1912

Type: Two-seat twin-engined monoplane
Notes and Structure: It is an unfortunate fact that little is known about this aircraft and indeed no photographs of it have come to light. The pages of *Jane's All the World's Aircraft* failed to carry a description or illustration. From what can be assimilated, it appears to have been basically a monoplane version of the Short Tandem-Twin, powered by two 70 hp Gnome engines that were mounted in the nose and rear of the fuselage nacelle to drive tractor and pusher propellers respectively. Seating was provided for a pilot and passenger side by side. The landing gear had wheels and the monoplane was only flown from land, yet it was constructed as a naval aircraft undoubtedly for launching from vessels when fitted with flotation bags. The latter would have been expected either to keep the aircraft buoyant while waiting to be lifted back on board ship or might have been intended for emergency use only.

The Short monoplane No 2, for want of a better title, was flown during October and November and reportedly received the nickname *Double-Dirty* because of the castor oil liberally sprayed over the

S.38 TYPE

First flight: 4 November 1912

Type: Two-seat biplane trainer
Notes and Structure: The early pusher biplanes produced by Short Brothers were very successful and a number were still in regular use during the early war years. S.38, in particular, had an interest-

Data
Power plant: See NOTES
Wing span: 8.92 m (29 ft 3 in)
Wing area, gross: 17.28 m² (186 sq ft)
Length overall: 7.62 m (25 ft)
Propeller diameter: 2.51 m (8 ft 3 in)
Max level speed: above 52 knots (97 km/h; 60 mph)
Endurance: 5 h

Variant
Monoplane. Single example only, as described above.

crew by the engines when running. It must be assumed, therefore, that for test purposes at least the engines lacked suitable cowling hoods: Gnome rotary engines were well known for this spurting and the cowling hood fitted to the original Short monoplane was so placed to reduce discomfort to the pilot. As a naval aircraft ordered by the Admiralty, the Short monoplane No 2 was given the serial 12 in the new numbering system adopted after November 1912, although this same number has, in the past, been associated also with a Bristol Boxkite (probably one of those flown at Eastchurch by the Navy). Another factor in the numbering tangle is that the Short aircraft was never officially accepted by the Navy, instead being returned to Short Brothers for modification, where it remained. However, a list of aircraft belonging to the Naval Wing of the RFC for March 1913 included seven monoplanes, comprising one Blériot, two Deperdussin, one Etrich, one Nieuport and two Shorts.

Data
Power plant: See NOTES
Dimensions, weights and performances: Not available
Variant: Single example only, flown a few times during October and November 1912

ing career and was modified on several occasions. In its final form it became virtually the prototype for a production S.38 type, the latter with tapered outer wings and the first use of a forward elevator supported directly from the nose of the crew nacelle. All those built by Shorts became trainers with the Naval Flying School at Eastchurch, except for S.59 which remained at the factory and S.62 which went to the CFS in July 1913. S.61 is also

S.38 type, one of the six built by **Norman Thompson Flight Co in 1915**

worthy of special note as it was subsequently modified into a twin-float amphibious seaplane with an ingenious retractable beaching gear, as was S.51 (see Tractor biplanes). In addition, S.38-type trainers were built before and after the outbreak of the First World War by others; 12 were constructed at the Supermarine Aviation works as 1580–1591, six by White and Thompson as 3143–3148, 12 more by White and Thompson as 8530–8541, and six by Norman Thompson Flight Co as 8434–8439. All of these had the 60 kW (80 hp) Gnome engine fitted.

Data

Power plant: 37.25 kW (50 hp) or 60 kW (80 hp) Gnome rotary engine
Wing span: 15.85 m (52 ft)
Wing area, gross: 46.45 m² (500 sq ft)
Length overall: 10.82 m (35 ft 6 in)
Height overall: 3.51 m (11 ft 6 in)
Weight empty: *(50 hp Gnome)* 431 kg (950 lb); *(80 hp Gnome)* 476 kg (1,050 lb)
Max t/o weight 680 kg (1,500 lb)
Max level speed: *(80 hp Gnome)* 50 knots (93 km/h; 58 mph)
Endurance: *(80 hp Gnome)* 5 h

S.53 SEAPLANE

First flight: Early 1913

Type: Patrol seaplane
Notes and Structure: The first tractor biplanes built by Short Brothers for the Naval Wing of the RFC had mixed fortunes but established a basic configuration that served the manufacturer

Variants

S.54–S.62. Short-built biplanes with military serials 19 (S.54, flown by Churchill during his visit to the Eastchurch flying ground on 15 May 1915, Churchill having previously flown the original S.38), 28 (S.55 with 80 hp engine, still in use in 1916), 34 (S.56, originally with 50 hp Gnome and later 80 hp, used for armaments training), 62 (S.57 at Eastchurch in January 1916), 63 (Short S.58), 64 (Short S.60), 65 (Short S.61, converted into an amphibian) and 446 (Short S.62).
S.38 Type. Thirty-six built by other manufacturers, all with 60 kW (80 hp) Gnome engines. Could also be flown as three-seaters.
S.67. Two earlier Short pushers were rebuilt as side-by-side trainers, known as 'sociables', becoming Navy 152 and 190. Both had 60 kW (80 hp) Gnome engines. The former was at Yarmouth in 1914 and Eastchurch in 1916, at Yarmouth as a short-lived sea patrol type. The original aircraft from which these were derived are unknown. A 'sociable' built as new was Short's S.67, which was given serial 145, and this was used to test an Austro-Daimler four-cylinder engine of 48.5–52 kW (65–70 hp) that weighed 105 kg (232 lb).

throughout the First World War. By this time the Admiralty no longer relied totally on the goodwill of men like McClean to get its officers airborne in aeroplanes and had learned from its abortive attempt not to follow the German example of spending huge sums on rigid airships. Therefore, while the German Navy pressed on with the concept of deploying rigid airships capable of carrying bombs to Britain (the first being the *LZ18/L2,* launched in September 1913), the British Admiralty came down firmly on the side of aeroplanes.

At first the Admiralty appeared unsure of its role within the Royal Flying Corps, its Naval Wing seemingly needing to find a separate identity. By the beginning of 1913 the few aeroplanes in Navy service were mostly landplanes, some of which had taken part in Army manoeuvres the previous year. But British seaplanes had shown their capabilities for water operation since November 1911, the first occasion when Cdr Schwann demonstrated a water take-off flying an Avro.

No man more so than Horace Short saw the benefits of seaplanes to the Navy and was vigorous in his pursuance of this form of aeroplane. Seaplanes appeared to give the Navy the identity it required, and by the middle of 1913 coastal stations had been established at the Isle of Grain, Calshot, Great Yarmouth, Felixstowe, Cromarty and on the Firth of Forth in Scotland. By the outbreak of the First World War, nearly half the RNAS's aeroplanes were seaplanes.

In an attempt to improve upon earlier tractor seaplanes delivered to the Navy, Horace Short designed the S.53. Based upon the S.41 types, it was powered by a 60 kW (80 hp) Gnome engine that could be started from the cockpit. It featured improved floats and metal interplane struts for the non-folding wings, and accommodated two passengers side-by-side forward of the pilot. Given the Navy serial 42, it may have taken part in the first Navy manoeuvres using aeroplanes, in July 1913. However, the floats were inadequate for water conditions found in the Firth of Forth, where it was initially based in July, and thereafter had a wheeled undercarriage fitted for operation at an RFC airfield in Scotland. On 27 August 1914, having previously returned to England, it was one aircraft of Wg Cdr Samson's Eastchurch Squadron that went to France (the first RNAS squadron to do so), in the company of two Sopwith Tabloids, one Farman biplane, one Bristol biplane, two Blériots and three Royal Aircraft Factory BE 2s. None of these was armed, only the Astra-Torres airship No 3 belonging to the squadron carrying any weapons. Unfortunately, Samson flew it into a tree in the following month while serving at the Headquarters in Morbecque.

Data
Power plant: See NOTES
Wing span: 14.63 m (48 ft)
Length overall: 10.67 m (35 ft)
Wing area, gross: 36.23 m² (390 sq ft)
Weight empty: 544 kg (1,200 lb)
Max t/o weight: 894 kg (1,970 lb)
Useful load: 350 kg (771 lb)
Max level speed: 56 knots (105 km/h; 65 mph)
Stalling speed: 43 knots (80 km/h; 50 mph)
Endurance: 4 h

Variant
S.53. Single example of an improved seaplane, purchased by Admiralty as 42.

FOLDER SEAPLANES

First flight: 17 July 1913

Type: Patrol seaplane
Notes and Structure: The S.53, exhibited at the February 1913 Olympia Show, and other Short seaplanes, were sufficiently impressive for the Admiralty to order follow-on aircraft. Those that were built immediately after S.53 were of two distinct types and are therefore described separately, the first type covering large patrol seaplanes with 119 kW (160 hp) Gnome engines and folding wings (covered here) and the other encompassing smaller non-folders with 74.5 kW (100 hp) Gnome engines.

Two large Short seaplanes were initially ordered by the Admiralty, similar in configuration to the S.53 but of greater size and featuring stronger floats and larger engines. According to some sources, these could accommodate up to four persons. However, the normal accommodation was for two in tandem cockpits, the forward cockpit for the observer with a wireless and to his rear the pilot.

The first of these was S.63, originally without wing folding but subsequently given manually-folding wings. It was attached to HMS *Hermes* for the Navy's first ever Fleet manoeuvres involving aeroplanes, in July 1913, carrying Navy serial 81. A similar aircraft was S.64, operated from the spring of 1914 as 82.

A refinement of the design produced the S.65 and S.66, larger aircraft than S.63/S.64 but powered by the same type of engine. These were particularly important as they featured mechanically folding 3-bay wings, actuated from the cockpit. In Navy service these were numbered 89 and

S.64, Navy 82, moored at Spithead during the Naval Review of July 1914. To its rear is the non-folder 78

90. A further enlargement produced the most significant Folders, S.82 to S.86, which entered the RNAS from May 1914. These carried military serials 119 to 122 and 186. To one aircraft of this type went the honour of becoming the first aeroplane to release a standard naval torpedo. At the instigation of Sqn Cdr A. Longmore and Winston Churchill, S.84 (Navy 121) was given new arched cross struts to the floats in order to allow the attachment of a standard Navy 14-in torpedo. With such a weapon fitted, Short's test pilot Gordon Bell took off at Calshot on 27 July 1914 and released it, thus making aviation history. The following day Longmore repeated the experiment, thus making him the first serving officer in the world to release a torpedo from an aeroplane. These feats generated much excitement and the other four aircraft of this series were similarly modified. The importance of these experiments was to be demonstrated by the later Short Admiralty Type 184. During October 1914, 119 served on board the seaplane carrier HMS *Hermes*, while 120, 121 and 122 were assigned to HMS *Engadine*. It was the latter vessel, in the company of *Riviera* and *Empress* with eight destroyers and

S.83, Navy 120, being launched at Westgate in August 1914 (*G. S. Leslie*)

two cruisers for escort, that launched seaplanes to raid the Zeppelin sheds thought to be at Cuxhaven, on 25 December 1914. Included in the raid were 119, 120, 135 and 136 (see VARIANTS) carrying bombs. In fact the sheds were some miles south of Cuxhaven, at Nordholz. Still a single seaplane located the sheds, in fog, but its bombs fell wide of the target, falling among trees. Other aircraft of the force attacked secondary targets. So ended the famous Cuxhaven raid.

Data
Power plant: See NOTES
Wing span: *(S.63 and S.64)* 17.07 m (56 ft); *(S.65 and S.66)* 18.59 m (61 ft); *(S.82–S.86)* 20.42 m (67 ft); *(S.88)* 16.61 m (54 ft 6 in)
Wing area, gross: *(S.63 and S.64)* 51.10 m² (550 sq ft);) *(S.65 and S.66)* 56.67 m² (610 sq ft); *(S.82–S.86)* 64.10 m² (690 sq ft); *(S.88)* 52.95 m² (570 sq ft)
Length overall: *(S.63 and S.64)* 12.19 m (40 ft); *(S.65, S.66 and S.88)* 12.34 m (40 ft 6 in); *(S.82–S.86)* 12.80 m (42 ft)
Weight empty: *(S.63 and S.64)* 1,088 kg (2,400 lb); *(S.65 and S.66)* 1,134 kg (2,500 lb); *(S.82–S.86)* 1,383 kg (3,050 lb); *(S.88)* 1,361 kg (3,000 lb)
Max t/o weight: *(S.63 and S.64)* 1,406 kg (3,100 lb); *(S.65 and S.66)* 1,542 kg (3,400 lb);

(*S.82–S.86*) 1,588 kg (3,500 lb); (*S.88*) 1,678 kg (3,700 lb)
Max level speed: 64–68 knots (119–126 km/h; 74–78 mph); (*S.88*) 63 knots (116 km/h; 72 mph)
Endurance: 5–6 h
Armament: S.82 to S.86 capable of launching 14-in torpedo. 20 lb bombs.

Variants
S.63 and S.64. Initial version with manually-folding wings. Navy serials 81 and 81.
S.65 and S.66. Larger improved versions with mechanically-folding wings and larger rounded fins. Navy serials 89 and 90.
S.82 to S.86. Largest and final version of Folder. Navy serials 119 to 122 and 186. Aircraft 121 used

on first torpedo-dropping experiments.
S.87 and S.88. These are believed to be the Short manufacture numbers of the Navy's 135 and 136 Folder seaplanes which followed earlier Folders into service from July 1914. Because of problems with the 119 kW (160 hp) Gnome 14-cylinder engine, 135 was fitted with a nine-cylinder 100.5 kW (135 hp) Canton-Unnè built by Salmson and weighing 276 kg (608 lb) and 136 a 14-cylinder 149 kW (200 hp) Salmson Canton-Unnè weighing 300 kg (661 lb). The latter served on HMS *Ark Royal*, which arrived off the Dardanelles on 17 February 1915 to launch 136 on a reconnaissance of Turkish positions. (*Ark Royal* was the first ship to be converted to a seaplane carrier before completion.) 136 was lost in April 1915.

S.80 NILE SEAPLANE and S.81

First flight: (S.80) 2 October 1913

Types: Four-seat expedition biplane and later dual-control trainer (S.80), and testbed for large guns (S.81)
Notes and Structure: After the failure of the S.32 hybrid, it became clear that a purpose-designed aeroplane would be the only practical answer to meet the demanding requirements of the McClean/Spottiswoode expedition up the Nile to Khartoum. The two most important features of the

resulting S.80 were the spacious four-seat fuselage nacelle and the adoption of a large 119 kW (160 hp) Gnome engine. Designed to be capable of modification from a twin-float seaplane to a landplane, the S.80 was an unequal-span biplane (folding wings) with twin rudders under a tailplane and elevator. An S.38 production type forward elevator was fitted initially. Under the rudders were carried two flotation bags, on which the aircraft's tail rested before taxiing for take-off. They also kept the S.80's tail from the water when semi-beached.

Before being transported to Alexandria (El

A series of photographs showing the S.80 Nile Seaplane during various stages of the expedition, the last with the aircraft beached for repairs to the floats and engine at Gananita Island

Iskandariya) on the Nile delta, Egypt, S.80 was flown with five persons on board, so proving its carrying capability. The distinguished crew for the expedition included McClean as pilot, Alec Ogilvie (pilot's certificate No 7 and purchaser of the second Short-Wright) as co-pilot and Horace Short who was certainly no stranger to adventure. The S.80 arrived at Alexandria on 27 December 1913 and was made ready for the start of the expedition. The first stage was begun on 3 January 1914 and Khartoum was eventually reached on 22 March, both the S.80's airframe and engine having been repaired several times during the expedition. Two days later S.80 was dismantled and it eventually went back to Eastchurch. There it was converted into a dual-control seaplane trainer for the RNAS, flying in this form from July. Modifications had included the substitution of new wings, deletion of the forward elevator and modifications to the tail unit. McClean presented it to the RNAS (with his earlier S.32) on the day Germany declared war on Russia, the aircraft becoming 905. Two months later it was re-engined with a 74.5 kW (100 hp) Gnome-Monosoupape and given a further tail unit update, which included rudders of greater area and the addition of an above-tailplane fin.

The very last pusher biplane of Short design was

the S.81 'Gun-carrier', a similar aircraft to the S.80, ordered for the RNAS for gunnery experiments (military serial 126). This used a 119 kW (160 hp) Gnome engine and was configured as a seaplane with additional wingtip stabilising floats. It was used initially to test a Vickers 1½-pdr quick-firing gun, mounted near the nose of the nacelle, then later a Davis 6-pdr gun.

Data
Power plant: See NOTES
Wing span: 20.42 m (67 ft)
Wing area, gross: 50.17 m² (540 sq ft)
Length overall: 10.29 m (33 ft 9 in)
Weight empty: 998 kg (2,200 lb)
Max t/o weight: 1,633 kg (3,600 lb)
Max level speed: 62 knots (116 km/h; 72 mph)

Variants
S.80. The first seaplane to fly along the Nile. Initially a four-seater with a 119 kW (160 hp) Gnome engine. Later a seaplane trainer with RNAS, re-engined with a 74.5 kW (100 hp) Gnome-Monosoupape.
S.81. Single example for the RNAS, used for gunnery experiments. 119 kW (160 hp) Gnome engine.

ADMIRALTY TYPE 74 SEAPLANES

First flight: (Type 74) 4 January 1914

Type: Patrol seaplanes (S.68: racing seaplane)
Notes and Structure: In addition to the large Folder seaplanes with 119 kW (160 hp) engines, the Admiralty ordered seven smaller seaplanes with non-folding wings and 74.5 kW (100 hp) Gnome engines. These are best remembered as Type 74s, 74 being the naval serial number of the first example. Like the later Folders, these had three-bay unequal-span wings, but they also adopted the small triangular tailfin of the early Folders and McClean's S.68 (see below).

All seven Type 74s appeared within one month of 4 January 1914 and were operated initially at Dundee, Clacton and Westgate, taking part in the July Naval Review. The Gnome engines were, however, troublesome and so these fourteen-cylinder double-row engines, each weighing 100 kg (220 lb), were exchanged for Gnome Monosoupapes. The latter nine-cylinder engine

used a valve that acted as exhaust and air intake, the petrol being taken in through ports in the

Admiralty Type 74 seaplane 76 off Gravesend in 1914, with Cdr Samson as pilot and the Rt Hon Winston Churchill (the First Lord of the Admiralty) as passenger, both in the forward cockpit

cylinder walls inside the crankcase. The Monosoupape was far more reliable and was well received. These seaplanes were given Navy serials 74 to 80.

In addition to the original seven (Short S.69 to S.75), a further four were taken by the Navy in July 1914 as military 180 and 183. These are believed to have been Short's S.76 to S.79 but were almost certainly built from spare components because of the threat of war in Europe. Three used Gnome Monosoupape engines but S.70 was completed with a 60 kW (80 hp) Gnome. A further eight aircraft were known as Improved Type 74s but these were based on the S.87/Navy 135 and as such can be found in the entry dealing with the Admiralty Type 166 and Types 827/830 seaplanes.

The only civil seaplane of this type was Frank McClean's S.68, in fact the first of the non-folders to emerge from the Eastchurch factory and intended to compete in the *Daily Mail* Hydro-Aeroplane Trial. This competition required an all-British aeroplane to cover the 1,337 nm (2,478 km; 1,540 miles) around the UK. As number 15 in McClean's personal fleet of aircraft, it was built with a favoured 67–74.5 kW

(90–100 hp) Green engine weighing 204 kg (450 lb). This aircraft was not successful and was tested with unequal- and equal-span wings. The Trial began on 16 August 1913, by which time McClean had withdrawn his entry. In the event it probably was not too great a disappointment, as only Harry Hawker began the journey, which had to be completed in a fortnight. Hawker's effort ended with a crash near Dublin.

Data (Type 74)
Power plant: See NOTES
Wing span: 17.37 m (57 ft)
Wing area, gross: 53.88 m² (580 sq ft)
Length overall: 11.89 m (39 ft)
Height overall: 3.58 m (11 ft 9 in)
Weight empty: 953 kg (2,100 lb)
Max t/o weight: 1,225 kg (2,700 lb)
Max level speed: 56 knots (105 km/h; 65 mph)
Endurance: 5 h

Variants
Type 74. Patrol seaplane. As described above.
S.68. McClean's biplane for the *Daily Mail* Hydro-Aeroplane Trial.

ADMIRALTY TYPES 166, 827 and 830, and S.310-type SEAPLANE TRAINERS

First flight: (Type 166) 1915

Types: Torpedo attack seaplanes and seaplane trainers (S.301–S.310 only)
Notes and Structure: The success of Navy seaplanes 135 and 136, especially the latter, naturally led to orders for production versions with the reliable Salmson-built Canton-Unnè engines or nine-cylinder Gnome Monosoupapes: in 1914 five makes of foreign engine were agented for or built in Britain, including the Canton-Unnè by the Dudbridge Ironworks of Stroud, Gloucestershire, a company with an office in Victoria Street, London, and the Gnome, available via the Gnome Engine Company, also of Victoria Street.

The larger and most powerful seaplanes of the production batches were those based on the excellent 136, using 149 kW (200 hp) Canton-Unnè engines, and these were generally similar to 136 except for being marginally larger and heavier and with wing refinements which included upper ailerons with inverse taper. Short Brothers produced

Westland 220 Canton-Unnè, the major production version of the Short Admiralty Type 166

One of the original Type 166s built by Short Brothers being lifted from its hangar on HMS *Ark Royal* and lowered into the sea

A further twenty Type 166s were sub-contracted to Westland. Early experience with the Short Type 166s had shown them to be of little or no use as torpedo carriers but performed well with bombs. The first major task for Westland Aircraft's embryo design department was to revise the float mounting of the Type 166, to delete provision for a torpedo but allow for the carriage of three 112-lb bombs. This was a greater task than it at first appears, as few working drawings were available from Short Brothers. Westland knew its Type 166s as Short 220 Canton-Unnès, whereas Short's name for its six production examples was the Type A. Westland aircraft were delivered from Yeovil from July 1916 and received Navy serials 9751 to 9770. The observer in the rear cockpit of each Westland aircraft was provided with a Lewis machine-gun and six drums of ammunition. One aircraft, 9754, was later modified into a landplane while serving in the Aegean theatre of war.

More than one type of seaplane fulfilled the requirement for a production 135 type, although each was closely related and differed mainly in the type of engine fitted. Including those constructed by other manufacturers, they were operated in various theatres of war and three even took part in the famous Cuxhaven raid on Christmas Day 1914. For some inexplicable reason the first eight built by Short Brothers (a batch which included the three used on the Cuxhaven raid) were known to the Admiralty as Improved Type 74s, military designated 811 to 818. Unlike the actual Type 74s, these had folding wings. The engine chosen was the 74.5 kW (100 hp) nine-cylinder Gnome Monosoupape. The next batch of three, military serials 819 to 821, covered similar aircraft with 100.5 kW (135 hp) Canton-Unnès and known as Admiralty Type 830s, this designation coming from the last serial of three more identical aircraft numbered 828 to 830. While the two batches of

just six as S.90 to S.95, and these received the military serials 161 to 166. Known as Admiralty Type 166s, they were flown from HMS *Ark Royal* from the end of 1915 and were used to spot for Royal Navy warships and bomb enemy shore positions in the Aegean Sea. During this episode 163 and 166 were also fitted temporarily with wheeled undercarriages for shore work from one of the small islands off the Greek coast.

One of the second batch of Type 827s built by Shorts, carrying the original Union Jack identification ordered for all RNAS aircraft on 26 October 1914. Type 827s proved particularly successful during the East African campaign

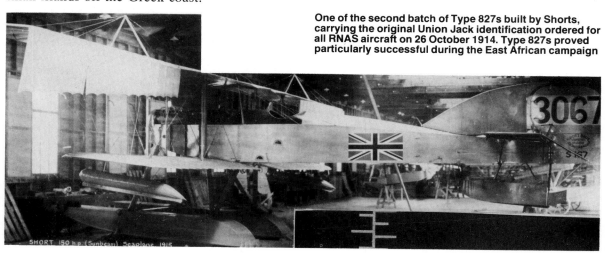

three were identical, the Type 830s themselves differed from the Improved Type 74s in other ways than engine choice, changes which included the adoption on each of a larger-area and more rounded tailfin. A further batch of twelve Admiralty Type 830s was delivered from May 1915.

Far more important than the Type 830 was the Type 827, the type number coming from the last machine of the initial batch of six built by Short Brothers with the new 112 kW (150 hp) Sunbeam Nubian engine. This engine, produced by the Sunbeam Motor Car Company at Wolverhampton, was also known as the Sunbeam-Coatalen after the company's chief engineer Louis Coatalen. It was an eight-cylinder Vee engine weighing 277 kg (610 lb) and produced its 150 hp at 2,000 rpm. Short Brothers completed a further thirty Type 827s as 3063–3072 and 3093–3112, while Brush Electrical built two batches as 3321–3332 (12 aircraft) and 8230–8237 (8), Parnall and Sons 8218–8229 (12) and 8250–8257 (8), Fairey Aviation 8550–8561 (12) and the Sunbeam Motor Car Company 8630–8649 (20). These aircraft were well used for patrol flights from RNAS stations on the east coast of Britain, although at least 8226–8229 fulfilled training roles, having been built with dual controls. Others served abroad from Royal Navy ships as patrol bombers and spotters, including service in Mesopotamia and Zanzibar. A small number of Type 827s were transferred to the Belgian government and flown by volunteers in the African colonies. 8560 was subsequently transferred to the RFC but was not the only example to be flown at one stage or another on a land undercarriage.

The last seaplanes of this general type were ten unarmed trainers (S.301–S.310) with 100.5 kW (135 hp) Canton-Unnè engines and modified wings; the centre-section of the larger upper wing was left uncovered.

Data
Power plant: See NOTES
Wing span: *(Type 166)* 17.45 m (57 ft 3 in); *(Types 827, 830 and S.310-type trainer)* 16.43 m (53 ft 11 in)
Wing area, gross: *(Type 166)* 53.23 m² (573 sq ft); *(Types 827, 830 and S.310 type)* 47.01 m² (506 sq ft)
Length overall: *(Type 166 and S.310 type)* 12.37 m (40 ft 7 in); *(Types 827 and 830)* 10.74 m (35 ft 3 in)
Height overall: *(Type 166)* 4.29 m (14 ft 0¾ in); *(Types 827 and 830)* 4.11 m (13 ft 6 in)
Weight empty: *(Type 166)* 1,588 kg (3,500 lb); *(Type 827)* 1,225 kg (2,700 lb); *(Type 830)* 1,190 kg (2,624 lb)
Max t/o weight: *(Type 166)* 2,077 kg (4,580 lb); *(Type 827)* 1,542 kg (3,400 lb); *(Type 830)* 1,508 kg (3,325 lb)
Max level speed: *(Type 166)* approx 56 knots (105 km/h; 65 mph); *(Type 827)* approx 53 knots (98 km/h; 61 mph); *(Type 830)* approx 61 knots (112 km/h; 70 mph)
Endurance: *(Type 166)* 4 h; *(Types 827 and 830)* 3½ h
Armament: *(Type 166)* Lewis machine-gun on flexible mount in rear cockpit, with six drums of ammunition. Three 112 lb bombs normally.

Type 166. Based on 136. Known to Short Brothers as Type A and Admiralty as Type 166. 26 aircraft.
Improved Type 74. Admiralty name for eight Short-built seaplanes with Gnome-Monosoupape engines. Known to Short Brothers as Type C. Three in Cuxhaven raid.
Type 827. 108 production aircraft with 112 kW (150 hp) Sunbeam engines, mostly built by other manufacturers. Some still in use in 1918.
Type 830. 18 production aircraft with 100.5 kW (135 hp) Canton-Unnè engines. Pilot in rear cockpit.
S.301–S.310. Short manufacture numbers for ten trainers used at Calshot from 1916. Pilot in rear cockpit.

ADMIRALTY TYPE 184

First flight: 1915

Type: Two-seat torpedo-bombing and patrol seaplane

Notes and Structure: The Admiralty Type 184 was one of the most important seaplanes to be used during the First World War, serving from 1915 until the Armistice and beyond, finally being retired from the RAF (formed after the amalgamation of the RFC and RNAS on 1 April 1918) in about 1921 following the delivery of Fairey IIIBs and Fairey Campanias. Gaining its type number from the military serial of the prototype produced by Short Brothers, it was that very aircraft that claimed the first ship ever sunk by a torpedo launched from an aeroplane. This historic event happened on 12 August 1915 when 184, operating from HMS *Ben-My-Chree* and crewed only by Flt Cdr C. H. Edmonds because of weight problems with the large 14-in Whitehead torpedo, attacked a 5,000 ton Turkish supply ship from an altitude of just 4.5 m (15 ft) above the Sea of Marmara, off Gallipoli, during the Dardanelles campaign. It was claimed at the time that the British submarine *E14* had already immobilised this ship some four days before and that another British submarine had actually struck the same ship with a torpedo simultaneously with Edmonds'. If, on this occasion, there is doubt as to the actual torpedo that sent the Turkish ship to the bottom, there was no doubt on 17 August, when Edmonds torpedoed a Turkish steamer a few miles north of the Dardanelles. The same day his colleague, Flt Lt G. B. Dacre, flying the second Type 184 seaplane (185), torpedoed a tug. Dacre's was a particularly unusual action, as he had been forced to alight his aeroplane because of engine problems but had taxied to his prey before releasing the torpedo. Thereafter he returned to HMS *Ben-My-Chree*.

These were the only successful torpedo actions involving Type 184s of the war; bombs later became standard armament, partly because of the aircraft's marginal performance with a torpedo. Subsequent bombing attacks included those against harbours and Type 184s operated in several far-off parts of the world as well as around Britain and Europe. Much of its best work involved spotting and reconnaissance and is remembered particularly for spotting and shadowing German warships on 31 May 1916, then gathering for the Battle of Jutland. On this occasion it was a Type 184 form HMS *Engadine* that spotted the thirteen German warships, and it can be claimed that this was the first time an aeroplane had been employed successfully in a naval action. This action prompted an official letter to be written to Short Brothers, an extract from which follows:

'. . . the flight made by Flight Lieut. Rutland, with Assistant Paymaster Trewin, as observer, which Sir David Beatty praises so highly, was carried out on a 225-h.p. "Short Seaplane" . . .'

One of the 75 Short-built Type 184s in the production series 8031–8105

Type 184 Type D 8103, powered by a 225 hp Sunbeam engine and featuring internal bomb stowage

This letter raised another interesting point, as the Type 184 was often referred to as the 225, which related to the power of its initial Sunbeam engine.

The Type 184 owes its being to Captain Murray Sueter of the Admiralty's Air Department who, in 1914, had been attempting to secure a seaplane for the Admiralty that could carry a Whitehead 14-in torpedo. Short Brothers was just one of three companies approached to develop (under a revised specification) a two-seat torpedo-carrying seaplane with wireless and a 225 hp Sunbeam engine, but its Type 184 was by far the most successful. Indeed, it was the first Short aircraft to be built in large numbers. Two prototypes were ordered with Navy serials 184 and 185, the first appearing in the early part of 1915 and all aircraft of the series thereafter being known collectively as Admiralty Type 184s. However, even before these prototypes flew, a further ten aircraft had been ordered for evaluation.

As originally built, the Type 184 was a large but fairly conventional seaplane, accommodating the pilot and observer/gunner in tandem. The most unusual feature of the design was the configuration of the equal-span and fully-folding wings, which tapered in chord from the tip to the roots. Large ailerons were fitted to the upper wings; later aircraft also had narrow chord ailerons on the lower wings. As for the wings, the wooden constructed fuselage was fabric covered. The tail unit comprised a conventional tailplane with elevators and a large-area rounded fin and balanced rudder. The twin main floats adopted cross struts with central arches to recess the torpedo, although straight cross struts were subsequently fitted as the torpedo

gave way to bombs. A single float supported the tail and air-bag wingtip floats were positioned under the outer interplane struts. The observer/gunner had use of a free-firing Lewis machine-gun and access to carrier pigeons to send off messages (including SOS signals!).

Because of the historical importance of the Type 184, on this occasion only a paragraph detailing the issued contracts follows. As will become clear, the great majority of Type 184s were built by other companies, as Short Brothers could not handle work on such a vast scale. However, Short Brothers received royalty on each aircraft built by other manufacturers. The 'Variants' section differentiates between models, later examples of which were given more powerful engines. By the Armistice the RAF still had 312 Type 184s in first-line service, the great majority with 260 hp Sunbeam inline engines. Each aircraft with engine cost under £4,500. Postwar, numbers were acquired by Japan, Estonia, Chile and Greece. Estonian aircraft remained flying until the end of 1933, the longest serving of any: in the early 1920s the Estonian Flying Service was divided into Land and Marine Wings, the latter consisting of the Shorts with 260 hp Maori engines, German Friedrichshafen FF 49s, M.IIs and a converted Halberstadt C.V fitted with floats. The Shorts, however, became of less and less importance to Estonia as the years passed.

Following the order for two prototypes (Navy serials 184 and 185), Shorts received a follow-on contract covering ten machines for evaluation (841–850). Thereafter Shorts received its largest single order for Type 184s, covering 75 (8031–8105). These were specified to have 225 hp Sunbeam engines but some flew with more powerful examples of Sunbeam engines. Of these, one

Improved Type 184 built by S. E. Saunders and Co in the Isle of Wight, powered by a 240 hp Renault engine and carrying two bombs on its under-fuselage rack

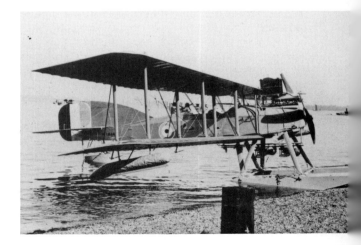

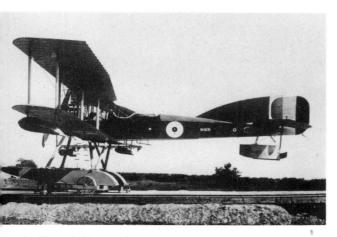

Phoenix Dynamo Manufacturing Co-built Improved 184

was a dual-control trainer, two went to France and one to Japan. However, S. E. Saunders had already received an order covering 30 Type 184s (8001–8030), 27 being completed with 225 hp Sunbeams and three with 240 hp Sunbeams, while Mann, Egerton received an order for 12 (8344–8355), Westland Aircraft 12 (8356–8367, one fitted experimentally with a 200 hp Mercedes engine), Phoenix Dynamo 12 (8368–8379) and Frederick Sage 12 (8380–8391). Delivery of Type 184s from other manufacturers began in November 1915, although major deliveries started in the following January. Thereafter Robey received a contract for 20 (9041–9060), delivered from mid-year; Sage 20 (9065–9084); Mann, Egerton ten 184 Type Bs with torpedo gear removed (9085–9094); Short Brothers ten Improved Type 184s with 240 hp Renault engines (N1080–N1089); Shorts ten Type 184s (N1090–N1099) with 240 hp Renault engines, except for one which had a 260 hp Sunbeam; Sage ten with 240 hp Renault engines comprising N1130–N1134 of Improved Type 184 model and N1135–N1139 of standard type; Saunders ten Improved Type 184s with 240 hp Sunbeams (N1140–N1149); Robey ten with Renault engines (N1220–N1229); Sage ten (N1230–N1239); J. S. White 20 Intermediates (N1240–N1259) with either 225 hp or 240 hp Sunbeam engines; Robey 20 (N1260–N1279) with 240 hp Sunbeams except for ten 225 hp Intermediates, a single 260 hp Improved and two 225 hp standard Type 184s; Shorts ten with 240 hp Renaults (N1580–N1589); Sage ten with 240 hp Renault engines except for one with a Sunbeam Maori (N1590–N1599); Saunders 21 with 240 hp Renaults (N1600–N1620) plus four with 260 hp Sunbeams (N1621–N1624); Phoenix Dynamo 30 Improved Type 184s (N1630–N1659) with 240 hp Renault

engines; Brush Electrical 30, all originally with 240 hp Renaults (N1660–N1689); Phoenix Dynamo 20, initially with 260 hp Sunbeam engines (N1740–N1759); Saunders 15 (N1760–N1774); Sage 20 with 260 hp Sunbeams (N1780–N1799); Robey 20 (N1820–N1839), seven with 240 hp Renault engines and the remainder with 260 hp Sunbeams; Brush Electrical 60 (N2600–N2659), plus 30 (N2790–N2819) with 260 hp Sunbeams; Robey 30 (N2820–N2849) with 260 hp Sunbeams, followed by 50 more (N2900–N2949); J. S. White 50 with 260 hp Sunbeams (N2950–N2999); Robey 60 with 260 hp Sunbeams (N9000–N9059); Brush Electrical 40 (N9060–N9099) with 260 hp Sunbeams; J. S. White 40 (N9100–N9139) with Sunbeam Maori engines, one with a 300 hp Manitou postwar; Robey 30 (N9140–N9169), all with 260 hp Sunbeams except a single example with one 275 hp Sunbeam Maori III; Supermarine 30 (N9170–N9199), of which it is thought that only 15 were delivered before contract cancellations, with 260 hp Sunbeam Maori engines; Brush Electrical 30 (N9260–N9289) with 275 hp Sunbeam Maori III engines; Robey 60 (N9290–N9349), of which only 16 were delivered; Brush Electrical 50 (N9350–N9399), all cancelled with Armistice; and J. S. White 50 (N9400–N9449), all cancelled. Interestingly, N2968, N2998, N9096 and N9118 became five-seat civil aircraft after the war, while a further aircraft (N2996) was civil registered but not flown as such.

Data

Power plant: (service standard aircraft)
One 168 kW (225 hp) Sunbeam
One 179 kW (240 hp) Sunbeam
One 179 kW (240 hp) Renault
One 194 kW (260 hp) Sunbeam
One 205 kW (275 hp) Sunbeam Maori III
Wing span: 19.36 m (63 ft 6 in); *(184 Type B)* 21.94 m (72 ft)
Wing area, gross: 63.92 m² (688 sq ft)
Length overall: 12.38 m (40 ft 7½ in)
Height overall: 4.11 m (13 ft 6 in)
Weight empty: *(260 hp Sunbeam)* 1,680 kg (3,703 lb)
Max t/o weight: 2,522 kg (5,560 lb)
Max level speed: *(260 hp Sunbeam)* 76 knots (142 km/h; 88 mph)
Climb to 1,980 m (6,500 ft): nearly 34 min
Service ceiling: 2,745 m (9,000 ft)
Endurance: 2 h 45 min
Armament: One Lewis machine-gun in rear cockpit. Originally one 14-in Whitehead torpedo; later up to 236 kg (520 lb) of bombs carried on underfuselage rack.

Variants
Type 184. Standard version, as described above.
Improved Type 184. Type 184 featuring small modifications, including to the bracing wires. 240 hp Sunbeam or Renault engine.
Intermediate Type 184. Aircraft intended to be of Improved standard but with only some of the updates.
Type 184 Type B. Ten aircraft built by Mann, Egerton with much greater upper wing span, reduced-span lower wings with rounded tips and no ailerons, only two sets of taller interplane struts each side of the fuselage to allow for the Type B's increased gap, and other changes. No torpedo equipment.
Dover Type 184. A number of aircraft for service from the so-called Dover Patrol stations, featuring enlarged floats that slightly reduced performance but were better suited to rough water operation.
Type 184 Type D. 8103 kept at Rochester for experimental work. Flew as a single-seat bomber with pilot occupying rear cockpit and forward cockpit faired over to house nine 65 lb bombs

One of ten Type 184 Type Bs built by Mann, Egerton and Co with a new wing arrangement and other changes

attached vertically. A small number of other Type 184s similarly modified as low-drag bombers, but none built as such.

BOMBER

First flight: 1915

Type: Long-range heavy bomber
Notes and Structure: To Short Brothers went the honour of producing the first four-engined heavy bomber to be flown into action by the RAF during the Second World War, in the form of the Stirling. To the same company had gone, in 1916, the honour of equipping the RNAS and RFC with their first purpose-built heavy bombers, although in this instance the aircraft was a direct derivative of a seaplane and was intended for interim use only.

At the outbreak of the First World War the destruction of German military airships and sheds had been a major priority but, as the first overtures of the war were played, the German fleet at its well protected base at Kiel in the Baltic Sea became increasingly menacing. The RNAS, which had already shown itself to be a potent striking force, although severely restricted in its actions by the mish-mash of small aircraft at its disposal, looked for a bomber capable of undertaking long-range missions with a heavy warload. At that time no suitable aircraft existed but by early 1915 Short Brothers had developed large seaplanes intended for RNAS use as torpedo-bombers. While not ideal, Short Brothers was requested to develop a land-based variant of the seaplane, the latter which became the Type 184 in RNAS service. The resulting prototype Bomber had much in common with the Type 184 seaplane but featured new high aspect ratio wings of unequal span (ailerons on upper wing only) and a four-wheel nose undercarriage.

As the 184 was expected to carry and launch a Whitehead torpedo, it was reasonable to hope that the Bomber would be capable of carrying a good warload. For defence the observer/gunner in the forward cockpit was originally to stand up and fire a Lewis gun over the top of the upper wing; how he was expected to do this in combat with the pilot manoeuvring the aircraft can only be guessed! During trials Bomber prototype 3706 flew reasonably but, like the Type 184, had the greatest difficulty flying with two crew and the specified warload. As a consequence, the wing span was increased by 3.66 m (12 ft), which made the Bomber unpleasant to fly. Nevertheless, the situation was desperate and 50 production Bombers were ordered from Short Brothers and 20 from the Sunbeam Motor Car Company, with 186.5 kW (250 hp) Rolls-Royce Eagle III and 168 kW (225 hp) Sunbeam engines respectively.

While Horace Short was abroad, the prototype was secretly modified by the addition of a 'plug' to lengthen the fuselage. On his return he found the

Bomber prototype 3706, the upper view showing the
original short-length fuselage, the centre view depicting
the Bomber with the original 2-bay wings and Lewis gun
position, and the bottom photograph shows the very
wide-span appearance of the Bomber when fitted with
extended 3-bay wings

lengthened bomber to possess improved stability
but gave his approval only after reassuring himself
of the safety of the modification. Several of the
companies that took part in the manufacture of
Short seaplanes also built Bombers to follow-on
orders, including Phoenix Dynamo, Parnall and
Mann, Egerton. As some aircraft were cancelled
after early examples of the fully purpose-designed
Handley Page O/100 appeared for heavy bombing, production of the Bomber was restricted to 83
machines (when including the prototype), of which
Short's contribution was 36. It is likely that all
Bombers that went into operational service from

1916 had the longer fuselage. The first went, in
very small numbers, to No 7 Squadron of the
RNAS's 5th Wing. Further deployment by the
RNAS was temporarily held up by an RFC request
to hive-off Short Bombers for the Somme offensive which began on 1 July. In fact only 15 were
handed over to the RFC but delays in getting the
Bomber fully operational with the RNAS meant
that Sopwith 1½ Strutters became the first equipment of No 3 Wing which, thus equipped in July,
became the first British strategic bombing unit.

In production form the Short Bomber was
equipped to carry eight 112 lb bombs or smaller
65 lb bombs when longer range was an operational
requirement. The pillar-mounted Lewis gun of the
prototype gave way to a standard rear-cockpit

Bomber 9315. This aircraft was built by Short Brothers
and was among those handed over to the RFC for the
Somme offensive

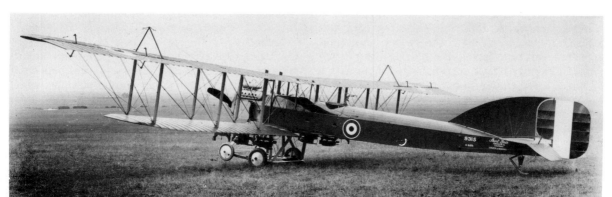

mounting for the Lewis gun, the pilot occupying the forward cockpit. No 3 Wing was the first to use the Bomber against strategic targets and Bombers continued to operate at night until superseded by O/100s. The date when the Bomber was retired is not entirely clear, although No 5 Wing began receiving O/100s in November 1916 and No 7 Squadron in early 1917. However, the first attack by O/100s in RNAS service was not achieved until mid-March 1917 and so it can be concluded that Bombers flew operationally until the spring of 1917 at least. In addition, a single aircraft from the Short-built batch of Bombers was presented to the French government for evaluation with the Air Force.

Data
Power plant: See NOTES
Wing span: 25.60 m (84 ft)

Wing area, gross: 80.83 m² (870 sq ft)
Length overall: 13.72 m (45 ft)
Height overall: 4.57 m (15 ft)
Weight empty: 2,268 kg (5,000 lb)
Max bomb load: 417 kg (920 lb)
Max t/o weight: 3,084 kg (6,800 lb)
Max level speed: 67 knots (124 km/h; 77 mph)
Service ceiling: 2,895 m (9,500 ft)
Endurance: 6 h
Armament: One Lewis gun plus up to 417 kg (920 lb) of bombs of 65 lb, 112 lb or 230 lb types.

Variant
Bomber. Interim land bomber for RNAS, derived from Admiralty Type 184 seaplane. Described above.

Short Brothers *SS3* submarine scout airship

SS3

First flight: 1915

Type: Non-rigid Submarine Scout airship
Notes and Structure: In September 1912 the British Admiralty purchased the Willows IV, a 27.43 m (90 ft) long non-rigid airship powered by a 26 kW (35 hp) JAP engine. This was sent to Farnborough for modification into the Naval Airship No 2, where the control surfaces were moved from the boom and positioned on the stern of the enlarged envelope. In this form it reappeared in 1913 and became a school airship until mid-1914. At this point the original passenger car was removed and replaced with a new car having dual controls and accommodation for three persons. In this form it made a single flight.

Later, the new Anzani engine was replaced with a Renault. In March 1915 the airship was again modified, this time having the fuselage of a Royal Aircraft Factory BE 2c aeroplane as the car with a 52 kW (70 hp) engine. It re-emerged on 18 March as the *SS1*, the first of a new series of small non-rigid airships intended to deal with the German U-boat menace and also hunt mines. The first sta-

tion for SS airships was set up at Capel near Folkstone.

The second SS (Submarine Scout) airship was built by Airships Ltd but was not a success. The first of the production series proper was *SS3*, built by Short Brothers and the only such craft produced by the company. The first of 26 similar SS airships, it used the fuselage of a BE 2c aeroplane as the gondola car, fitted with a 52 kW (70 hp) Renault engine. *SS3* was very successful.

Data
Power plant: See NOTES
Length overall: 43.74 m (143 ft 6 in)
Max diameter: 8.50 m (27 ft 10 in)
Volume: 1,700 m² (60,000 cu ft)
Max speed: 42 knots (77 km/h; 48 mph)

Variant
SS3. Single example of a non-rigid airship built by Shorts. Thereafter the company supplied small component parts for other similar airships, which were assembled in Admiralty craft at Kingsnorth (where *SS3* was flight tested) and Wormwood Scrubbs.

First flight: July 1916

Type: Torpedo and patrol seaplane

Notes and Structure: This aircraft, sometimes also referred to as the 310 (both designations being derived from the horsepower rating of the Cossack engine in initial and later production forms), was intended to supersede the Type 184 as a torpedo plane after the earlier type had proved unsuited to this demanding role. This is not to say that the Admiralty planned to withdraw the Type 184. Far from it, as the Type 184 found an important part to play as a patrol aircraft. The main problem with the Type 184 as a torpedo carrier was its lack of engine power, resulting in limited range and pilot-only operation while armed with a Whitehead torpedo; the achievements of Edmonds and Dacre were not repeated by Type 184s.

The 320, which was to become the ultimate torpedo-carrying seaplane from Short Brothers of the First World War, as well as the company's last type of seaplane to see action in the war and its largest, was designed around a new engine then under development by the Sunbeam Motor Car Company and which became the Cossack. This twelve-cylinder engine initially gave an output of 231 kW (310 hp) but later production examples produced 239 kW (320 hp) normal rating. Engine weight was about 454 kg (1,000 lb). The Short 320 seaplane was to carry the new 18-in Mk IX torpedo, which weighed the same as the engine.

Short Brothers produced two seaplane designs, both clearly of the same ancestry to the Type 184. However, one was intended as a torpedo carrier while the other was for patrol with superior performance to the Type 184. Both were larger, strengthened and refined compared to the Type 184, the torpedo plane having unequal-span two-bay wings and a larger-than-normal (for Shorts) interplane gap. The pilot was accommodated in the forward cockpit, while the rear cockpit for the observer/gunner could carry two persons if required; subsequent trials with prototypes showed that the torpedo could only be carried when the pilot alone crewed the aircraft. The second design, for the patrol type, differed mainly in the use of equal-span three-bay wings.

The Admiralty ordered four prototypes from Short Brothers, as 8317–8320, of which the first two were torpedo carriers. These were known to Shorts as Type As and appeared in July and August 1916. By now German U-boats operating in the Mediterranean were causing increasing concern to the Admiralty and so these prototypes were sent out to the new RNAS base at Otranto to

N1397, a 320 built by Short Brothers

assist Type 184s in dealing with the U-boats as they slipped from their bases in the Adriatic. The Otranto base, being right on the east coast of Italy at a bottleneck point with Albania's west coast, was ideal for this operation. However, both 320s broke up during torpedo trials at Otranto, the cause of which was insufficiently strong float struts.

With the float strut arrangement revised, the Type A was put into production as the Short Type A4. Meanwhile the first of the patrol prototypes had appeared in September 1916 as 8319, but this version was not selected for production and 8319 became a testbed for large-calibre guns. The second example of the patrol type, intended to be 8320, was completed as an A4 with serial N1480, in fact the first aircraft of a later batch of twenty-five Short 320s (some of which went to the Japanese government). This batch followed earlier batches ordered from Shorts as N1150–N1159 and N1300–N1319, and N1360–N1389 from Sunbeam. Seven aircraft from the second Short-built batch went to Otranto and one to the torpedo training base at Malta, followed by other Short-built aircraft, while most Sunbeam aircraft went to home stations. The first attempt to torpedo submarines from Otranto was made on 2/3 September 1917, when six 320s were mounted on lighters and towed by boats to a position from which they would have sufficient fuel (with pilots only) to mount an attack on submarines lying off Cattaro. Unfortunately, although the first part of this operation went well, a gale wrecked the mission at the last moment and all 320s were lost before take-off. Thereafter most operations with 320s were of a patrol nature with bombs replacing the torpedo.

By November 1918 the service still had 50 320s in use, the last being withdrawn the following year. Despite real torpedo capability, the 320 never managed to achieve the reputation of the earlier Type 184 and, of course, was built in much smaller numbers.

Data

Power plant: See NOTES
Wing span: 22.86 m (75 ft); *(wings folded)* 7.01 m (23 ft)
Wing area, gross: 75.25 m² (810 sq ft)
Length overall: 13.94 m (45 ft 9 in)
Height overall: 5.33 m (17 ft 6 in)
Weight empty: 2,237 kg (4,933 lb)

Max t/o weight: 3,181 kg (7,014 lb)
Max level speed: 69 knots (127 km/h; 79 mph)
Climb to 3,050 m (10,000 ft): 50 min
Climb to 610 m (2,000 ft): 12 min
Service ceiling (with an 18-in torpedo): 915 m (3,000 ft)
Endurance: 6–7 h
Armament: One 18-in Mk IX torpedo or two 230 lb bombs. Most fitted with Lewis machine gun mounted level with the upper wing.

Variant

320. Two prototypes and 125 production aircraft, as described above.

N.2A and N.2B

First flight: (N.2A) 23 January 1917

Types: Experimental bombing seaplanes
Notes and Structure: In 1916 the Admiralty issued specification N.2A in the hope of acquiring new sea-going two-seaters of much better performance than the single-seaters then in RNAS service for scouting and bombing duties; the Sopwith Schneider and Baby could manage only one and two 65 lb bombs respectively. Among the designs submitted to the Admiralty were the Fairey N.2A, Handley Page H.P.14, Parnall Panther, Norman Thompson N.2a, and two from Short Brothers, the less ambitious Short seaplane being the work of Horace and the other from Oswald.

The Admiralty ordered two aircraft from Fairey as N9 and N10 (Fairey III) and six more with serials N76–N81, but none of the second batch was built. Handley Page received an order for six machines as N27–N32, the first two seaplanes and

N.2A in Scout No 1 form

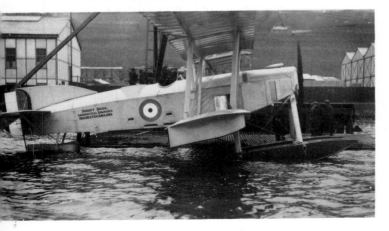

N30 deck-landing type only being built. A similar number of prototypes were ordered from Parnall as N91–N96. Only N37 was ordered from Norman Thompson and Short Brothers received an order for one as N36, with a 149 kW (200 hp) Sunbeam Afrida engine. Horace's seaplane was built as S.313 (Short manufacture number) Experimental Scout No 1. This was similar to existing Short seaplanes but was smaller to suit the conditions on board ship. It was basically a sesquiplane with an uncovered upper wing centre-section and a short fuselage. The radiator position was a novel feature, carried under the engine in a duct. As originally built this would not fly but, after being lengthened and renamed Experimental Scout No 2, it managed to take off. However it performed poorly and was dropped.

Oswald's Experimental Scout No 3 flew for the first time on 27 March 1917 as an equal-span biplane with a new low-drag wing section and elliptical wingtips, straight wing trailing-edges and a greater than usual (for Short aircraft) interplane gap. The fin was triangular in shape and of very small area, and a frontal radiator was adopted.

In tests this aircraft proved underpowered and so a 205 kW (275 hp) Sunbeam Maori I was fitted, but still it was inadequate to attract orders, not least because its bombload was no greater than that of the Sopwith Baby. As on Horace's N.2A, the rear observer/gunner had use of a Lewis gun. Interestingly, the Handley Page seaplanes were flown to Grain, during trials, by Gordon Bell. Only the Parnall Panther became operational as a carrier-borne spotter and reconnaissance aircraft from the N.2A types, and then only postwar.

When the Admiralty issued its specification N.2B for a patrol and bombing seaplane to replace the Type 184, Oswald submitted a new seaplane with a Maori I engine. On this aircraft the upper wing had no dihedral and had slight overhang over the dihedral lower wings, and the wings folded. The upper wing had inversely tapering ailerons while the lower wings were of reduced chord and, on the second aircraft, had rounded tips. The crew of two had tandem cockpits, the pilot seated under the wing centre-section in which a gravity fuel tank was carried. Again there was competition for orders and Short Brothers was asked to construct eight prototypes as N66–N73, although in the event only the first two were built. The first of these was Short's S.419, which appeared in December 1917. The second was S.420. Once more the Short seaplanes were not adjudged the best and the most important aircraft from the N.2B specification became the Fairey IIIB. In May 1919 N.2B N67 was re-engined with a 280 kW (375 hp) Rolls-Royce Eagle VIII, but this was done secretly without the permission of the Air Ministry. The Eagle served only to confirm Oswald's belief that the higher-rated engine was all that was needed to make the N.2B a first-rate aircraft. It is worth noting that from the Fairey IIIB came the IIIC, D and F, classic landplanes and seaplanes for the RAF and FAA during the interwar period.

Data
Power plant: See NOTES
Wing span: *(S.313)* 14.02 m (46 ft); *(S.364)* 11.89 m (39 ft); *(S.419 and S.420)* 16.81 m (55 ft 2 in)

Wing area, gross: *(S.313)* 41.81 m² (450 sq ft); *(S.364)* 34.84 m² (375 sq ft); *(S.419 and S.420)* 62.99 m² (678 sq ft)
Length overall: *(S.313)* 9.60 m (31 ft 6 in); *(S.364)* 8.53 m (28 ft); *(S.419 and S.420)* 12.24 m (40 ft 2 in)
Height overall: *(S.419 and S.420)* 4.19 m (13 ft 9 in)
Weight empty: *(S.419 and S.420)* 1,415 kg (3,120 lb)
Max t/o weight: *(S.419 and S.420)* 2,150 kg (4,741 lb) Maori engine
Max level speed: *(S.419 and S.420)* 80 knots (148 km/h; 92 mph), Maori engine; 76 knots (142 km/h; 88 mph), Maori engine at 3,050 m (10,000 ft)
Time to 1,525 m (5,000 ft): 12½ min, Maori engine; to 3,050 m (10,000 ft) 40½ min, Maori engine
Endurance: 4½ h
Armament: Lewis gun in rear cockpit plus bombs.

Variants
N.2A. Two aircraft, as described above. The first, by Horace Short, flown in two forms. Second aircraft by Oswald Short and built as S.364.
N.2B. Two prototype long-range patrol and bombing seaplanes, as described above. Disposable load apart from fuel was approximately 531 kg (1,170 lb).

N.2B N66 (S.419) at Rochester in early 1918

AIRCO D.H.9

First flight: (Short-built) 1918

Type: Two-seat bomber; used also for antisubmarine patrol and reconnaissance.
Notes and Structure: In 1917 the Airco D.H.4 biplane became operational with the RFC and RNAS as the first ever British warplane intended from the outset as a day bomber. This proved highly successful and the more powerful versions were capable of outpacing fighters. In July 1917 the prototype of the intended replacement flew for the first time as the D.H.9, featuring a Siddeley Puma engine and with the pilot's cockpit and that of the observer/gunner brought closer together to enhance communication. Unfortunately, the Puma engine that had promised 224 kW (300 hp) proved unreliable and had to be derated to 172 kW (230 hp). This loss of almost 24 per cent

in power greatly reduced the D.H.9's intended performance and made it inferior to the D.H.4. Nevertheless, more than 3,200 D.H.9s were built in Britain by many manufacturers, Short Brothers constructing 100 at Rochester with the military serials D2776–D2875.

Originally to be powered by Fiat A-12 inline engines of 224 kW (300 hp), it is probable that all were in fact completed with Pumas, although some sources quote Pumas, Fiat A-12s (the prototype installation of which was the work of Westland Aircraft) and 172 kW (230 hp) B.H.P.s. Of these, a small number was modified for experimental deck trials on board HMS *Argus* and *Eagle*, each aircraft featuring a nose radiator and carrying an air bag in the fuselage in case of an emergency ditching.

Data
Power plant: See NOTES

Wing span: 12.92 m (42 ft 4⅝ in)
Wing area, gross: 40.32 m² (434 sq ft)
Length overall: 9.30 m (30 ft 6 in)
Height overall: 3.40 m (11 ft 2 in)
Weight empty: 999 kg (2,203 lb)
Max t/o weight: 1,664 kg (3,669 lb)
Max level speed: 96 knots (177 km/h; 110 mph)
Service ceiling: 4,725 m (15,500 ft)
Endurance: 4½ h
Armament: One fixed forward-firing Vickers machine-gun. One or two Lewis machine-guns in rear cockpit on Scarff ring mounting. Up to 209 kg (460 lb) of bombs.

Variant
D.H.9. Total of 100 built by Short Brothers at Rochester in 1918.

Short-prepared civil floatplane version of the Airco D.H.9

FELIXSTOWE F.3 and F.5

First flight: (Short-built F.3) May 1918

Type: Anti-submarine and general reconnaissance flying-boat

Notes and Structure: In 1917 the Felixstowe F.2A anti-submarine patrol flying-boat entered production for the RNAS. It was based on the Curtiss H.12 but featured a redesigned hull conceived by Sqn Cdr John C. Porte. As Felixstowe was a seaplane experimental station only, manufacture of F.2As was entrusted to Airco, Norman Thompson and Saunders. A larger but slower and less manoeuvrable derivative became the F.3, which was capable of carrying twice the bomb load over greater distances. Short Brothers was awarded a con-

One of thirteen F.5s built by Short Brothers for the Imperial Japanese Navy

F.3 commercial conversion G-EAQT at Rochester in May 1920

tract to construct 50 such flying-boats, each with two 280 kW (375 hp) Rolls-Royce Eagle VIII engines strut-mounted between the unequal-span biplane wings.

The first hull from Short was launched from the construction yard at Strood and taken by river to the new final assembly works at the existing Rochester factory, where the completed aircraft was launched. However, by the Armistice not a single Short-built F.3 had been flown in anger with the newly formed RAF. Nevertheless, production continued into 1919, when the last of 35 F.3s was completed. The final part of the contract had earlier been modified to cover the improved F.5, which incorporated several Short-developed refinements to improve sea-going qualities. Meanwhile a second order for fifty flying-boats (all F.5s) had been placed with Shorts but this was reduced, postwar, to just ten, the last of which flew in March 1920. Interestingly, none of the F.5s ordered from Phoenix Dynamo (with military serials immediately before those allocated to the Short F.5s) was completed, all having been cancelled along with 50 from May, Harden and May and 50 with Liberty engines as F.5Ls from Dick Kerr.

The delivery of the final ten F.5s to the RAF did not signify the end of Short Brothers' involvement with this type of flying-boat. Having had forty F.5s cancelled, Shorts completed 12 similar aircraft for the Imperial Japanese Navy, the final batch of three with Napier Lion engines of 335 kW (450 hp) rating. Short Brothers' personnel also helped with the construction of one F.5 in Japan, using local materials, and Aichi subsequently produced a further 50 in that country at the Yokosuka works near Nagoya. These took over from previously-used Tellier flying-boats in IJN service. Finally, Shorts also refurbished ex-RAF F.3s for sale abroad as civil aircraft and serviced RAF operational F.5s. An F.5 with a metal hull was flown in 1925 as the Short S.2 (see VARIANTS).

Data (F.3)
Power plant: See NOTES
Wing span: 31.09 m (102 ft)
Wing area, gross: 131.27 m² (1,413 sq ft)
Length overall: 14.99 m (49 ft 2 in)
Height overall: 5.72 m (18 ft 9 in)
Weight empty: 3,610 kg (7,958 lb)
Max t/o weight: 5,550 kg (12,235 lb)
Max level speed: 79 knots (146 km/h; 91 mph)
Service ceiling: 2,440 m (8,000 ft)
Endurance: 5–6 h normal; more than 9 h max
Armament: Gunners' positions in the bow and under the upper wing trailing-edge, with two Lewis machine guns each. Usually four 230 lb bombs under the wings.

Variants
F.3. Original Felixstowe flying-boat constructed under contract by Short Brothers. N4000 was the first ever flying-boat built by the company.
F.5. Second type of Felixstowe flying-boat built by Short Brothers for the RAF and the Imperial Japanese Navy. Incorporated Short refinements.
S.2. Towards the end of 1924 Shorts won a contract from the Air Ministry for an experimental modern derivative of the F.5 with a duralumin metal hull. This was allocated the military serial N177, a serial within the N1–499 original batch of numbers set aside for experimental naval seaplanes. Another new feature was that the S.2's Vee bottom hull framing incorporated some longitudinal members of arched form, a design then recently patented. In other respects the S.2 was a typical F.5. First flown on 5 January 1925, the S.2 was Short's first large flying-boat with a metal hull. It flew well as an experimental aircraft with the

The experimental S.2 (N177), the first large Short Brothers' flying-boat with an all-metal hull

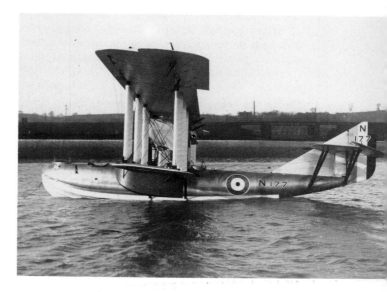

Artist's impression of the projected twin-hulled flying-boat, that appeared in the 1919 edition of *Jane's All the World's Aircraft*

RAF, proving that any extra weight of a metal hull could be offset by no water soakage, although Shorts considered that subsequent hulls could be of lighter weight.

Additional Notes
The 1919 *Jane's* included an artist's impression of a twin-hull flying-boat of huge dimensions and powered by two tractor- and one pusher-mounted Rolls-Royce Condor engines carried on the centre plane of triplane wings. This was never built but was intended as a 30-passenger aircraft with dining section. It was also intended to have stowable berths for night services. Short Brothers had to return to a more conventional configuration before eventually securing orders for a commercial flying-boat of large size. Interestingly, the Italian company, Savoia-Marchetti, built successful twin-hulled multi-engined flying-boats during the 1930s.

SHIRL and S.538 ATLANTIC Shamrock

First flight: (Shirl) 27 May 1918
(Shamrock) 8 April 1919

Type: Carrier-borne torpedo biplane (Shirl)
Notes and Structure: In the latter part of 1916 Commodore Murray Sueter, the founding father of British torpedo aeroplanes, conceived the idea of flying landplanes armed with torpedoes from suitable seaplane carriers. This concept first led to the introduction of the Sopwith Cuckoo, the first-ever deck-flying torpedo plane, which went to sea on board the aircraft carrier HMS *Argus* less than a month before the Armistice.

Meanwhile, the Admiralty had issued specification N.1B but there is some confusion as to whether it applied to deck-operating torpedo aircraft, scouts or both. Certainly both Short Brothers and Blackburn constructed three prototypes each of their deck-operating torpedo biplane designs to an Admiralty order of 1917 but it is thought that this specification was not N.1B, which covered single-seat flying-boat fighters from Blackburn (its so-called Nib) and Supermarine (Baby) and the Westland N.1B Scout Seaplane.

The Short Shirl prototypes and the Blackburn Blackburds were designed as single-seaters with 280 kW (375 hp) Rolls-Royce Eagle VIII engines, each capable of launching the large 1,423 lb Mk VIII torpedo. Unlike the lighter Whitehead or Mk IX, the Mk VIII torpedo had the capability of knocking out a major warship.

As the Shirl was ordered before it was possible for large warplanes to land back on board ship (the flat-top HMS *Argus* had still to be commissioned), it was designed to have a wheeled undercarriage which could be dropped after take-off to allow the release of the torpedo and safe ditching in the sea for recovery following the mission. The fuselage was plywood covered. The wings were similar to those of the N.2B's, except that the upper had dihedral and constant-chord ailerons were fitted to upper and lower surfaces.

Following S.421's initial flights (S.421 being the Short manufacture number for the first Shirl, allocated military serial N110), it was tested officially but thereafter returned to Rochester for modification. Here it received noticeable wing sweepback and a new main undercarriage, the latter comprising a divided gear with flotation air-bags (inflated by compressed air in an emergency) carried over skids, with small hydro vanes to the front of the skids and releasable twin wheels on each unit to prevent the aircraft from turning over when alighting on water. Equally important was that the new undercarriage allowed the torpedo to be released without the aircraft losing its ability to make a conventional landing on shore, if range allowed. In this revised form S.421 flew again in July 1918.

The second Shirl (S.422) appeared soon after the reworked S.421, carrying the military serial N111. This introduced changes to the tailplane and had ailerons of greater area, but was initially less successful than the first. It was used in trials against the Blackburn Blackburd but in the event neither type was adjudged suitable for service, partly because of a lack of manoeuvrability, and more Cuckoos were ordered. A contract previously placed with Blackburn for production of 100 Shirls was, therefore, cancelled.

The third Shirl (S.423, military N112) appeared at the end of 1918. After a short time it was no longer required as an experimental torpedo carrier, so Short Brothers proposed the conversion of this aircraft into a long-range type to attempt the first non-stop transatlantic flight and thereby win the £10,000 *Daily Mail* prize. However, the Shirl was not released for this purpose and it was tested instead as an experimental mailplane, with a large container for ½-ton of mail carried on the torpedo attachment.

Short Brothers was not to be denied a chance at the *Daily Mail* prize and so built an aircraft similar to the Shirl for this purpose alone. Known to Shorts as the S.538 Atlantic and named *Shamrock*, it had three-bay wings of greater span and area, a larger tailplane, it adopted a cross-axle undercarriage, and carried a huge fuel tank under the fuselage. First flown on 8 April 1919, its first attempt at the crossing to Ireland for the start of the transatlantic flight ended in an unscheduled ditching.

The final Shirl prototype, N112, with the ½-ton mail container

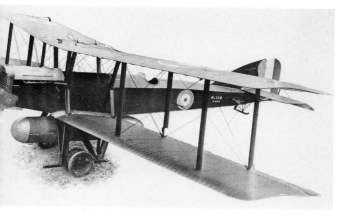

S.538 Atlantic *Shamrock* being readied for its first flight at Grain. Note the large fuel tank suspended under the fuselage

Thanks to its Shirl ancestry, it remained buoyant for the time required to tow it ashore (nearly a day) but before it could be readied for another attempt the prize and honour had gone to a Vickers Vimy flown by Capt John Alcock and Lt Arthur Brown, who landed in Ireland from Newfoundland on 15 June 1919. The crew of the two-seat *Shamrock* was Maj J. C. P. Wood and Capt C. C. Wyllie who, if their engine had not failed them, might have become household names.

Data
Power plant: See NOTES
Wing span: *(Shirl)* 15.85 m (52 ft); *(S.538)* 18.95 m (62 ft 2 in)
Wing area, gross: *(Shirl)* 73.49 m² (791 sq ft); *(S.538)* 94.30 m² (1,015 sq ft)
Length overall: *(Shirl and S.538)* 10.67 m (35 ft)
Disposable load apart from fuel: *(Shirl)* 1,134 kg (2,500 lb)
Weight empty: *(Shirl)* 1,293 kg (2,850 lb)
Max normal t/o weight: *(Shirl)* 2,699 kg (5,950 lb); *(S.538)* 3,810 kg (8,400 lb)
Max level speed: *(Shirl)* 86 knots (159 km/h; 99 mph)
Cruising speed: *(S.538)* 69 knots (129 km/h; 80 mph)
Climb to 3,050 m (10,000 ft): *(Shirl)* 30 min
Endurance: *(Shirl)* 6½ h normal
Range: *(S.538)* approx 2,779 nm (5,150 km; 3,200 miles)
Armament: *(Shirl)* One 1,423 lb Mk VIII torpedo

Shirl. Experimental torpedo plane. Three proto-types. 100 production aircraft expected to be built by Blackburn (allocated serials N7550–N7649) but none constructed. Final Shirl modified into an experimental mailplane.

S.538 Atlantic 'Shamrock'. Similar aircraft to Shirl but with greater-span wings and tailplane, more fuel carried in a tank under the fuselage and with accommodation for two persons, for attempt at non-stop transatlantic flight.

R31, R32, R37 and R38

First flight: *(R31)* August 1918

Type: Military rigid airships

Notes and Structure: Despite the destruction of the Vickers *Mayfly* (the first rigid airship built in Britain) before a single flight had been made, Vickers was responsible for all the next five rigid airships launched in the UK during 1916 and 1917. The first of these to appear after the *Mayfly* of 1911 was the Vickers No 9, and it was upon this design that Short Brothers was contracted to construct two airships for the Admiralty, work beginning in 1916. However many revisions to the project were made before Short Brothers finally got underway with its *R31* and *R32*.

As a result of the many revisions, the *R31* and *R32* were based upon Schütte-Lanz principles furnished to the Admiralty by a Swiss engineer. However, the structure of the airships bore no resemblance to that of the pre-war Schütte-Lanz trellis system and was analogous to that of Zeppe-lins as adopted for later Schütte-Lanz airships. Each of the main girders in the *R31* and *R32* consisted of three plywood sides, lightened with slots at regular intervals, which were glued to spruce angle-members more or less of V-section. The triangular girder was strengthened internally by plywood diaphragms. This method of construction was used for all varieties of girders, including those of square and rectangular sections. The girders were attached to ring-frames constructed in a similar way. Casein cement, known by its German name *Kaltleim*, was adopted as the adhesive for most of *R31*'s construction and for *R32*, although the former airship used some gelatin cement before *Kaltleim* became available to Shorts. The gas-bags were made of rubber-proofed cotton fabric, lined with goldbeaters skin. A keel corridor extended from end to end inside the bottom of each airship hull, serving to support and distribute the weights of petrol, water ballast, etc. The control car under the bow of each airship was divided into three compartments; forward the navigating cabin, next the wireless compartment, and then the officers' sleeping quarters aft. Initially *R31* was tested with six boat-built gondolas, arranged in

R31 in original configuration for its maiden flight, with six Eagle engines

R32 at Cardington

pairs, each with a 186.5 kW (250 hp) Rolls-Royce Eagle engine installed. However, one of the rear gondolas was removed and the remaining one slung parallel with the centre-line. Reversing gears were fitted to amidships engines.

R31 was launched from the purpose-built Cardington shed in August 1918 as a six-engined craft. Before its next flight in October, the five engine layout had been adopted. It was commissioned on 6 November that year but on its delivery flight the gelatin cement failed at certain points and the *R31* was taken instead to the shed at Howden. This building lacked a roof and the *R31*'s wooden frame suffered from bad weather and neglect and had to be declared dangerous in 1919. *R31* had flown for just nine hours! It was subsequently sold for scrap.

R32 was commissioned on 3 September 1919 and, although a sister to *R31*, was highly successful. It first served in an experimental capacity at the National Physical Laboratory and then was assigned as a crew training ship for US Navy personnel for six months from October 1920. Having flown for about 260 hours, it was deleted in 1921 after the shut-down of the British Airship Service and was destroyed in a controlled experiment.

Shorts' *R37*, a duralumin framed rigid airship

taken over from Vickers, was never completed and the *R38*, ordered from the company just before the end of the First World War, was taken over as a Service Airship Factory type after work on its design had started. However, a number of Short Brothers' employees remained at Cardington thereafter to assist with its completion and it was finally launched on 23 June 1921 (see Introduction for further details of the *R37* and *R38* and 1919 and 1920 editions of *Jane's All the World's Aircraft*).

Data *(R31 and R32)*
Accommodation: Crew of 21
Power plant: See NOTES
Length overall: 187.45 m (615 ft)
Max diameter: 19.96 m (65 ft 6 in)
Volume: 43,976 m³ (1,553,000 cu ft)
Gross lift: 47.1 tons
Disposable lift: 16.4 tons
Max level speed: 56 knots (105 km/h; 65 mph)
Cruising speed: 40 knots (74 km/h; 45 mph)
Range: more than 1,737 nm (3,218 km; 2,000 miles)
Armament: Machine guns for defence in several positions.

Variants
R.31. First Short-built rigid airship. Completed 9 hours flying. Deleted because of a rotting wooden framework.
R.32. Successful rigid airship, flown 260 hours between September 1919 and 1921. Sister ship to *R31*.
R.37. Metal (duralumin) framed airship taken over from Vickers. Never completed.
R.38. Contract with Short Brothers cancelled but airship completed thereafter as Service Airship Factory type, with assistance from Short employees. The first airship with a volume of more than 2½ million cu ft (77,600 m³; 2,740,000 cu ft).

The metal-framed R37 (left) and R38 during construction at Cardington in 1919

SHRIMP SPORTING TYPE SEAPLANE

First flight: 10 December 1919

Type: Utility seaplane

Notes and Structure: The twin-float seaplane that eventually became known as the Shrimp was derived from the design of a seaplane trainer for the RAF, two prototypes of which are believed to have been allocated the military serials N97 and N98. However, these military prototypes were cancelled in the early part of 1918 and the serials were transferred to two Coastal Experimental No 1 aircraft produced by the Royal Aircraft Factory.

The Shrimp was built by Short Brothers as its first new post-war aircraft type and, according to the 1920 *Jane's*, was viewed as suitable for military and civil uses. It was an equal-span biplane, the upper wing without dihedral. The upper and lower wings had constant chords and used metal spars and plywood ribs, fabric covered. The neat fuselage was a semi-monocoque structure of plywood, with a fabric top decking. The main floats had hollow bottoms and produced very little wash, while to beach the aircraft an axle could be passed through prepared holes in the floats and wheels attached at each end. In this way the Shrimp could be handled easily by two or three persons. A tail float was carried under the extreme rear fuselage. Another feature of the Shrimp was its use of the Short Patent Folding Wing System, which permitted its storage in small sheds or hangars.

Accommodation was unusual, with the forward cockpit seating two in tandem with dual controls, while the rear cockpit had two seats side by side. Shorts, therefore, viewed the aircraft as entirely suitable for such military tasks as flying instruction and gunnery/wireless/photography/bombing tuition. In civil form it was suitable to flying instruction, passenger carrying or the transportation of small quantities of freight.

In civil form the Shrimp was expected to use a 119 kW (160 hp) Beardmore engine, while for war work a 172 kW (230 hp) Siddeley Puma of the type Shorts fitted to its contract-built D.H.9s was seen as ideal. It was with the Beardmore that the first example of the Shrimp flew, constructed as S.540 and registered G-EAPZ. This aircraft was subsequently re-engined with the Puma and was used by Frank Hurley on survey flights of the New

S.540 Shrimp (with a Beardmore engine) using its beaching wheels in late 1919

72

Guinea coast from Australia between 1922 and 1923.

A second Shrimp had, in the meantime, flown as G-EAUA, with the follow-on registration being reserved for a third. The second was Short's S.541. This first flew in July 1920 with a Puma engine and dihedral on both sets of wings. After a few months it was damaged and later reappeared with a 224 kW (300 hp) Hispano-Suiza engine weighing 270 kg (595 lb), compared to the Puma's 288 kg (636 lb), plus full-span variable-camber flaps. However, this aircraft was not the most successful of the Shrimps built.

The third Shrimp was S.542, not flown until January 1921. It was powered by a Puma engine and featured upper and lower wing dihedral but without the full-span variable-camber flaps of S.541. No buyer could be found for this aircraft and it was broken up with S.541 in 1924.

Data
Power plant: See NOTES
Wing span: 13.56 m (44 ft 6 in); *(folded)* 4.57 m (15 ft)

Wing area, gross: 47.38 m² (510 sq ft)
Length overall: 11.20 m (36 ft 9 in)
Height overall: approx 3.66 m (12 ft)
Weight empty: *(160 hp Beardmore)* 950 kg (2,095 lb)
Payload: 218 kg (480 lb)
Max t/o weight: *(Beardmore)* 1,406 kg (3,100 lb); *(Siddeley Puma and Hispano-Suiza)* 1,612 kg (3,554 lb)
Max level speed: *(Beardmore)* 72 knots (133 km/h; 83 mph); *(Puma)* 82 knots (153 km/h; 95 mph); *(Hispano-Suiza)* 87 knots (161 km/h; 100 mph)
Climb to 3,050 m (10,000 ft): *(Beardmore)* 35 min
Range: 234 nm (435 km; 270 miles)
Armament: None carried. Military examples were expected to carry a machine gun in the rear cockpit and practice bombs or cameras when required.

Variant
Shrimp. As described above.

SILVER STREAK

First flight: 20 August 1920

Type: Experimental all-metal biplane
Notes and Structure: Few aircraft in history can have been so advanced for their time and yet suffered more from official prejudice than Short Brothers' Silver Streak biplane. Proven to be sound of limb, not prone to distortion or deterioration, and possessing good handling and fine performance, it was nevertheless flown only over a period of a few days in official hands. It never received a Certificate of Airworthiness and never bore its later-allocated military serial, and all because of its all-metal construction.

Oswald Short, whose more extravagant ideas had been partly suppressed by his eldest brother until Horace's death in 1917, conceived the idea of an all-metal aeroplane in 1919. This concept was not a wild fancy but one he considered to be within the capability of the company, bearing in mind previous research into the behaviour of metal structures and Short's contributions to the *R37* and *R38* duralumin-structured rigid airships. Flying in the face of those who considered duralumin unsuitable for the primary structure of an aeroplane, construction of an experimental prototype began in early 1920, the resulting aircraft being of wonderfully streamline appearance but basically a conventionally configured biplane.

Oswald's concept of producing something more durable than wood and fabric, and yet as light and strong, also had other foreseen advantages, not least of which was the aircraft's non-inflammable material and ability to operate in varying climatic conditions without concern. Another plus was the

Silver Streak on show at Olympia in July 1920, when it was still known as the Swallow

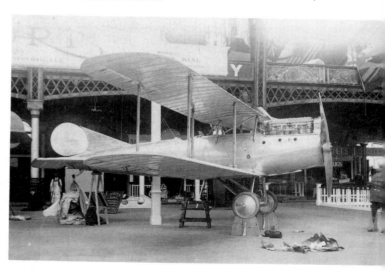

Silver Streak during its initial flight trials at Grain, with John Parker in the cockpit

possibility of rapid production using stamped out components. Known originally as the Swallow, the prototype was built entirely of duralumin, with the exception of the wing spars and a few other minor parts in which it was found that steel was a more suitable material. As built, the Silver Streak was a single-seat tractor biplane with two-bay wings, having been designed to carry mail or light freight up to a weight of 181 kg (400 lb). If required, the design allowed for two passengers to be accommodated in place of the mail.

The fuselage was virtually a streamline duralumin tube suitably stiffened with bulkheads, rings and longitudinals. Where holes were cut in the shell the edges were stiffened by rolls of sheet duralumin. This structure was thoroughly tested and proved sufficient to withstand the necessary tail loads. It was built up of duralumin sheets, riveted to oval channel-section formers of a heavier gauge. On the inside of the formed tube, corrugated longitudinal stiffeners of sheet duralumin were riveted to the skin at intervals around the circumference. At the fore end, the oval formers were replaced by four very strongly built box-section brackets, open at the top and supporting the two steel-tube bearers on which the 179 kW (240 hp) Armstrong Siddeley Puma engine was mounted. Immediately aft of the Puma, a solid duralumin bulkhead closed off the engine from the rest of the fuselage.

Immediately under the bulkhead the steel tube front spar root was carried, and a second bulkhead further to the rear served to take and distribute the loads from the rear spar roots. These two spar roots carried at their outboard ends a box rib of the same section as the wing. The upper wing cabane, of steel tube construction, was a pair of inverted Vees. This carried the elementary upper wing centre-section which consisted of one duralumin box rib and a pair of stub spar sockets. Aft of the second bulkhead was the pilot's cockpit. At the rear of the fuselage, bulkheads to support the tailplane and the oval-rudder post were built in.

The wings were built on tubular steel tubes of 50-ton steel. Duralumin ribs, lightened with circular holes, slipped on to the spars and were secured by small pins passing through the spar holes of the ribs and the spar tube itself. These ribs had no flanges. Instead they were deeper throughout the chord than was the wing profile proper and the covering sheets of duralumin (originally aluminium, but these buckled in a flight test and were replaced), and turned upwards at their edges. The covering strips were of such width that one intervened between each rib, and each rib had small tongues cut and turned on alternative sides for the cover to rest on. These were then capped by a trough-section strip and the five thicknesses were riveted through from outside the wing. Damaged covering strips could therefore be removed and replaced with no disturbance to any other part of the wings, and special riveting tools were unnecessary.

Over that portion of the wing which carried ailerons, the ribs terminated on a small diameter duralumin tube somewhat aft of the spar proper. Projecting past this tube were a number of stout duralumin box ribs, and the ailerons were hinged to these ribs, the hinge itself carried back into recesses cut in the ailerons, which were thus balanced by the part projecting forward of the hinge. The elevators were similarly hinged and balanced. The tailplane was built in a similar way to the wings, on tube spars with duralumin ribs, duralumin covered. The tailplane spars were sufficiently strong to do without the then-usual bracing; despite this there was bracing from the lower side of the rear fuselage to the tailplane.

The undercarriage was of the steel-tube V-type with a cross axle, which was sprung on rubber in the normal way. In addition, there was built into the base of each V an oil dashpot with a plunger attached to the axle, which formed an anti-bouncing snubber (this worked very well indeed).

When completed, the Silver Streak was exhibited at the Olympia Show of July 1920 and after this was returned to Rochester for flight testing. Although Oswald had been unable to gain initial financial support for the project from the Air Ministry, this official body later became sufficiently interested to purchase the aircraft for evaluation of the structure. The date for the purchase is thought to have been 23 December. However, before delivery Silver Streak was modified into a tandem two-seater, the original aluminium wing covering having already been superseded by duralumin. Sent to Farnborough in February 1921, it underwent rigorous ground tests and made its only official flights during four days of June. However, flying had shown it to possess really excellent performance, and an extensive series of mechanical tests proved the structure to have the necessary strength, together with an extraordinary resistance to long-continued vibra-

Air Ministry-owned Silver Streak two-seater about to make its delivery flight to Farnborough on 1 February 1921, with Parker as the pilot and Oscar Gnosspelius in the forward cockpit

tions of a magnitude quite beyond those expected from normal use. The satisfactory result of all trials led, in early 1922, to the Air Ministry placing a firm order for two prototypes of an armed derivative. This derivative was seen as a possible future replacement aircraft for the Bristol F.2B Fighter of the First World War vintage, still in production as an army co-operation type. Intended to use Jaguar engines, these prototypes were cancelled in July as part of a round of economy cuts, leaving Bristol Fighters to continue service with the RAF for many more years (after which they gradually gave way to the Jaguar-engined and completely conventional Armstrong Whitworth Atlas).

Short Brothers still considered there was a chance of getting an all-metal aircraft into production, if not in Britain then in the North American

Model of the projected North American seaplane with Napier Lion engines (Charles E. Brown)

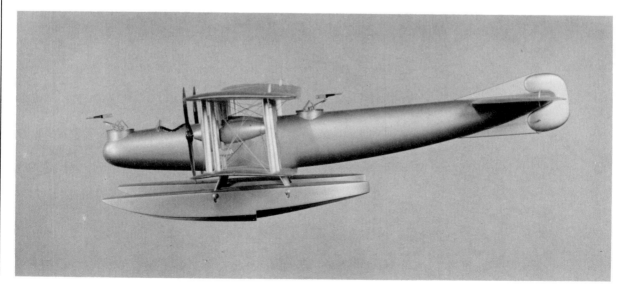

continent. The company set about designing a twin-engined seaplane of similar construction. However, once again no orders followed and this time not even a prototype was constructed.

Data

Power plant: See NOTES
Wing span: 11.43 m (37 ft 6 in)
Wing area, gross: 34.37 m² (370 sq ft)
Length overall: 8.05 m (26 ft 5 in)
Height overall: 3.20 m (10 ft 6 in)
Weight empty: 846 kg (1,865 lb)
Fuel and oil: 193 kg (425 lb)
Useful load: 181 kg (400 lb)
Max t/o weight: 1,302 kg (2,870 lb)
Max level speed: 109 knots (201 km/h; 125 mph)

Cruising speed: 78 knots (145 km/h; 90 mph)
Climb to 3,050 m (10,000 ft): 11 min
Range at full power: 313 nm (579 km; 360 miles)
Range at cruising speed: 391 nm (724 km; 450 miles)
Endurance at full power: 3 h
Endurance at cruising speed: 5 h

Variants

Silver Streak. Single prototype. Civil registration G-EARQ allocated but never used as C of A not awarded. Subsequently received military serial J6854.
Twin-engined all-metal seaplane. Project only to interest North American customers. Not built.

N.3 CROMARTY

First flight: 19 April 1921

Type: Anti-submarine patrol and bombing flying-boat
Notes and Structure: To fulfil a wartime Admiralty (later RAF) requirement for a large patrol flying-boat capable of taking off and alighting in rough water, to be moored out in slightly protected harbours, and of staying away from its base for long periods, Short and Vickers submitted designs which became the Cromarty and Valentia respectively. Although three prototypes of each design were ordered, the end of hostilities brought a cutback to just one of each type.

Short's Cromarty was influenced by the Felixstowe F.3, for which the company had received a wartime order. However, the Cromarty was larger and incorporated several innovations. The hull,

The Cromarty was the first Short Brothers' flying-boat of original design

though of spruce with plywood covering over the lower portion and with a fabric-covered top decking, was the most important update. Instead of the usual Vee bottom, the planing surface was concave each side of the keel. This was intended to allow a more gradual entry into the water and reduce shocks without the loss of planing efficiency caused with a Vee hull by the outward spraying of water. It was still a biplane with the greatest span on the upper wing, which had large unbalanced ailerons, and power was provided by two big 447 kW (600 hp) Rolls-Royce Condor engines. A biplane tail unit was adopted with auxiliary rudders flanking the large central fin and rudder. The pilot and co-pilot were accommodated in an open cockpit on side-by-side seats, while the main defensive position was mid-way between the wings and the tail. The bow position was occupied by the gunner/bombardier, who was to operate a 37 mm automatic anti-submarine gun.

The single Cromarty prototype took about two years to construct, owing to the lack of urgency after the Armistice. Already three military serial numbers from the original N1–499 experimental seaplane batch had been allocated to the Cromarty and three to the Valentia, of which only N120 (Cromarty) and N124 (Valentia) were used. The single Cromarty was launched in March 1921 and first flew in the following month. The single Valentia was tested from the Solent initially but, like the Cromarty, was evaluated by the Marine Aircraft Experimental Establishment at Grain. However, in June 1922 the Valentia crashed.

After its appearance the Cromarty was continually revised, leading eventually to the installation of uprated 485 kW (650 hp) Condor engines (driving four-blade propellers from the crashed Valentia). In final configuration the Cromarty was well received by the Seaplane Development Flight

but unfortunately it was damaged beyond worthwhile repair in 1922, having been taxied on to a reef by mistake, and was beached on the Isles of Scilly.

So ended the first Short-designed flying-boat. A commercial derivative of the Cromarty had also been planned as an 18-passenger flying-boat with a crew of five. Included in the data below are some specifications relating to the Commercial Cromarty, inserted for interest.

Data
Power plant: See NOTES
Wing span: 34.59 m (113 ft 6 in); *(Commercial Cromarty)* 34.14 m (112 ft)
Wing area, gross: 208.38 m² (2,243 sq ft)
Length overall: 17.98 m (59 ft); *(Commercial Cromarty)* 18.29 m (60 ft)
Height overall: 6.71 m (22 ft)
Normal t/o weight: 8,165 kg (18,000 lb)
Max t/o weight: 8,981 kg (19,800 lb)
Max level speed: 83 knots (153 km/h; 95 mph)
Economical cruising speed: *(estimated for Commercial Cromarty)* 78 knots (145 km/h; 90 mph)
Range: 782 nm (1,448 km; 900 miles); *(estimated for Commercial Cromarty at econ cruising speed for 6 h flight with a 1,722 kg/3,796 lb commercial payload)* 469 nm (869 km; 540 miles); *(estimated for Commercial Cromarty at econ cruising speed for 11 h flight with a 581 kg/1,280 lb commercial payload)* 860 nm (1,593 km; 990 miles)

Variants
N.3 Cromarty. Single prototype built as Short's first flying-boat of original design.
Commercial Cromarty. Projected commercial version of the Cromarty. Not built.

S.3 SPRINGBOK

First flight: 19 April 1923

Type: Two-seat fighter biplane
Notes and Structure: In the early 1920s the RAF's fighting strength was dominated by the Bristol F.2B Fighter, a two-seater that had seen much action during the First World War from 1917. Thousands were built during that war and production continued until 1927 to maintain the RAF's strength for its 'air control' policing duties on the North-West Frontier of India and in Iraq. Others

served in Germany, Egypt, Palestine, Syria and Turkey.

Although F.2Bs operating in tropical climates were specially equipped for emergencies and crew survival, a worrying problem was the deterioration of the aircraft's structure in such conditions. The Bristol Aeroplane Company also considered the Fighter not to be entirely suited to these overseas duties and produced a possible replacement as the Jupiter Fighter, although this was little more than an F.2B fitted with a Bristol Jupiter in place of the normal engine. The Jupiter Fighter remained a prototype. However, as mentioned in the pages of

Springbok I with original tailfin and metal skinned wings

this book detailing the Silver Streak, the Air Ministry had, even before air control duties began in Iraq on 1 October 1922, decided to investigate further the Short all-metal aircraft at Farnborough.

At the end of 1922 the Geddes Committee, which had only a few months earlier recommended that the two Short prototypes be cancelled, issued a new report suggesting that the prototypes to Air Ministry Specification 19/21 should be completed after all. One outcome of the delay was the selection of the powerful 400 hp Bristol Jupiter IV nine-cylinder radial engine for the prototypes, as fitted to the Jupiter Fighter. (Interestingly the Jupiter engine, which proved so successful for Bristol, had been designed by Roy Fedden and was originally produced by Cosmos Engineering before that company went into liquidation and Bristol took over the patent rights.)

The two prototypes from Short Brothers were known as S.3 Springboks and were very similar in construction and design to the Silver Streak, except that the upper wing roots met the fuselage and the lower wings were no longer neatly faired into the fuselage but continued beneath supported by short struts. This wing arrangement made it necessary for the centre-section of the upper wing to be uncovered and clear for the benefit of the pilot, while the observer/gunner occupied a cockpit fitted with a Scarff ring and twin Lewis machine guns. The fixed forward armament was a single Vickers gun. Another change from the Silver Streak was the tail rudder, which was less circular in design. Both prototypes subsequently had their deep tailfins redesigned to increase area.

Both prototype Springboks were initially flight tested by John Lankester Parker at Martlesham Heath, on 19 April and 24 July 1923 respectively. However, even before the second S.3 flew, the first had been returned to the Short Brothers' works at Rochester after the metal covering on the wings had split at the trailing-edges due to vibration. When this Springbok flew again in September it had fabric-covered wings. Meanwhile the second aircraft had also been modified, but by the use of a heavier gauge of metal on the trailing edges.

Testing of the prototypes continued after official acceptance but the second aircraft crashed and its pilot killed. The investigation that followed led to an order for six further prototypes in revised S.3a Springbok II form, an order thereafter halved. The first of these flew on 25 March 1925. Each Springbok II differed from the original prototypes in having fabric-covered wings, the upper wings attached to a raised fuselage and the bottom wings secured directly to the lower fuselage, an arrangement much closer to that of the Silver Streak. However, the lower wings were of much reduced chord, resulting in the interplane struts no longer being parallel. Two small rectangular sections of the lower port wing were uncovered to allow a reconnaissance camera to be fitted

Springbok II J7295. Note the concave panel in the port fuselage side to allow the pilot a clear downward view through the rectangular sections of the lower wing

or to assist in bomb-aiming. Set into the upper wings were two gravity fuel tanks, so placed to reduce fire risk and undoubtedly also to keep them clear of ground fire which was common during air control operations. The tail unit was completely revised and fabric covered, with balanced elevators and a new taller fin and rudder of greater area, the latter horn-balanced.

The three Springbok IIs were delivered for official testing but no production followed. Instead, the first of these was reworked by Short Brothers into the Chamois Corps reconnaissance prototype.

Data
Power plant: As above
Wing span, both: *(Springbok I and II)* 12.80 m (42 ft)
Wing area, gross: *(Springbok I)* 43 m² (463 sq ft); *(Springbok II)* 42.74 m² (460 sq ft)
Length overall: *(Springbok I)* 8.20 m (26 ft 11 in);
(Springbok II) 8.99 m (29 ft 6 in)
Max t/o weight: *(Springbok I)* 1,851 kg (4,080 lb); *(Springbok II)* 1,937 kg (4,270 lb)
Max level speed: *(Springbok I)* 105 knots (195 km/h; 121 mph); *(Springbok II)* 107 knots (198 km/h; 123 mph)

Variants
Springbok I. Two prototypes, as described above. These were the first all-metal aircraft built to order for the RAF.
Springbok II. Developed version. Three built, as described above.

GNOSSPELIUS GULL

First flight: 26 May 1923

Type: Single-seat ultra light monoplane
Notes and Structure: In 1910 Oscar T. Gnosspelius designed and built his first full-size aeroplane. After the First World War he joined Short Brothers to head the newly formed experimental

The original Gnosspelius Gull G-EBGN

section of the company. As the result of a large number of experiments with models at the Short Brothers' works at Rochester, he designed a uniquely configured glider. Although intended to be built in this form at his own expense, the announcement of competitions for light powered aircraft flying on one gallon of fuel (that offered substantial prizes) attracted his attention and the glider design was converted into one for a single-seat powered lightplane with a 697 cc Blackburne

engine. This engine was of particular interest, as it had been developed to power motorcycles and was adopted for a number of aeroplanes flown in the 1923 Lympne Competitions. It was a two-cylinder 60° Vee twin fitted with overhead valve gear and an external flywheel. The cylinders were of cast iron and the pistons of aluminium alloy. It was remarkable for the high MEP (about 120 lb/sq in) developed at quite high speeds and for its good balance. Its weight with magneto and flywheel was only 33 kg (73 lb). However, later events proved the engine less than satisfactory in the Gull.

Built by Short Brothers, the Gull was one of the first light aeroplanes to fly in Britain. It had a distinctly bird-like form, with a circular-section fuselage and a sharply down-turned nose. The wing helped to further the bird-like appearance, having a short parallel-chord centre-section and cantilever outer-sections with leading edges that sloped back to the wingtips. The wings were fabric covered and were of a thin section built on four spars. The centre-section was braced by steel-tube struts to the front and rear of the spars and supported the engine. The two pusher propellers were chain-driven from the engine. A curious feature of the wings was the 'step' top surface at about one-third chord from the leading-edge. The fuselage was boat-built of very thin spruce planks carried on light elm hoops and the axle for the under-carriage wheels passed through the fuselage, leaving the wheels to half project through the bottom.

Flight testing was satisfactory and Short Brothers offered to build the Gull in series, but no orders were forthcoming. However, a second was built at company expense and both Gulls were entered for the Lympne Motor Glider Competitions, the first to be flown by Parker and the new aircraft by Rex Stocken. The competitions, spon-sored by the *Daily Mail*, took place at Lympne in Kent, England. These began on 8 October 1923, the very day the second Gull made its maiden flight.

Because of engine problems, both Gulls failed to cover the required distance to qualify in the main event, which was won by the English Electric Wren and ANEC monoplane, each of which flew 76 nm (140.8 km; 87.5 miles) on a single gallon of fuel: the Wren was powered by a 398 cc ABC engine, while the ANEC used a 1,100 cc Bristol Cherub. For a long period thereafter the Gulls lay idle but the second subsequently found its way to a group of enthusiasts from the Newcastle-upon-Tyne Light Aeroplane Club. With the group it was flown off and on for nearly four months before being written off in a fatal accident on 24 June 1926.

Data
Power plant: See NOTES
Wing span: 11.05 m (36 ft 3⅜ in)
Wing chord: *(max)* 1.68 m (5 ft 6 in); *(min)* 0.41 m (1 ft 4 in)
Wing area, gross: 13.19 m² (142 sq ft)
Length overall: 5.94 m (19 ft 6 in)
Weight empty: 163 kg (360 lb)
Max t/o weight: 259 kg (570 lb)
Max level speed: 61 knots (113 km/h; 70 mph)

Variant
Gull. Two examples only, as described above. Second flown at Martlesham on official trials after the Lympne Competitions, along with other light aircraft. (The importance of these trials should be noted, as the de Havilland D.H.53 Humming Bird, which was also flown at Lympne and then tested at Martlesham, was then ordered for the RAF for parasite aircraft experiments with airship *R33*. The D.H.53 too was Blackburne powered.)

S.4 SATELLITE

First flight: 10 September 1924

Type: Two-seat light monoplane
Notes and Structure: In 1924 there was a great surge of interest in light aircraft, partly due to the inspired Lympne competition of 1923 but also because of the announcement made on 1 September 1924 that the British Air Ministry intended to help finance the establishment of light aero-plane flying clubs throughout the UK. This put new impetus into the design of light aircraft and subsequently led to the incredible success of the de Havilland Moth biplane.

The original Motor Glider Competitions held at Lympne in 1923 certainly encouraged the design of light aeroplanes, but these were in the main impracticable single-seaters. A more ambitious attempt to encourage the design of light aircraft suitable for flying clubs was made by the Air Ministry with the announcement of its Two-Seat Light Aeroplane Trials in early 1924, to be held from 29 September to 4 October at Lympne. The

Parker in the forward cockpit of the S.4 Satellite

rules were simple but exacting. Each two-seater was to have folding wings, an engine of less than 1,000 cc, a minimum control speed below 39 knots (72 km/h; 45 mph) and a maximum speed of at least 52 knots (97 km/h; 60 mph).

Eighteen aircraft entered for the competitions, including a monoplane from ANEC with an Anzani engine, the Avro Avis biplane with a Cherub, the Beardmore Wee Bee monoplane with a Cherub, the good-looking Blackburn Bluebird biplane with a Blackburne engine, the Cherub-engined Bristol Brownie monoplane, the Cranwell C.L.A.2 Cherub-powered biplane, the Gloster Gannet biplane with a Blackburne engine, the ABC Scorpion-powered Hawker Cygnet biplane, two two-seat versions of the Parnall Pixie Blackburne-engined monoplane, the Cherub-engined Vickers Vagabond biplane, and two Cherub III-engined Woodpigeon biplanes from Westland. On the whole the biplanes looked far more workmanlike and indeed the Cranwell aircraft won a total of £300 on reliability trials, but the first two prizes overall went to the monoplanes from Beardmore and Bristol.

Short Brothers also designed and built an aircraft for the Trials as the S.4 Satellite, work on which began in July 1924. This was a monoplane with mid-mounted cantilever wings of composite construction, the spars being built up of laminated mahogany flanges and three-ply webs. The ribs were Warren girders of duralumin trough section. The chord of the wings was constant throughout the span, except for the rounded tips, but the sec-

tion tapered in thickness from roots to tips. Fabric covered the wings. Wing flaps extended over the whole span, used both as ailerons and as camber-changing devices.

The fuselage was built entirely of duralumin, the sheet metal skin supported by box or flanged sheet formers. The undercarriage was of divided axle type, hinged to a point at the bottom of the fuselage and supported by vertical telescopic legs running up to the front main spar root and braced by a pair of thrust tubes running backwards to the bottom of the fuselage.

The fabric-covered tail unit was conventional and was framed in steel tube with duralumin ribs. The fixed one-piece tailplane was carried across the top of the rear fuselage and braced by two pairs of struts. The elevator was divided and the rudder extended to the bottom of the fuselage. Power was provided by a Bristol Cherub engine rated at 24 kW (32 hp) and mounted on an aluminium casting attached to the fuselage front frame, with an interposed fire-proof bulkhead. A spinner was made for the propeller to match the engine cowling but it appears that most of the flying was done without the spinner and sometimes without the cowling. Two persons were accommodated in separate tandem cockpits.

During flight trials the Satellite proved easy to handle and possessed good performance with the pilot only on board but would not take-off with a passenger. Various modifications were tried to obviate this problem but in the event the Satellite failed in its attempt to make an impression on the competition.

81

During the course of its flying career thereafter the Satellite received three changes of engine: the first when a tuned Cherub was fitted for the 1924 Grosvenor Cup; early in the following year a geared Cherub II; and finally a 31 kW (42 hp) ABC Scorpion Mark II, after transfer to RAF officers at Eastchurch in 1926. The last engine was a two-cylinder horizontally-opposed type weighing 47.6 kg (105 lb) and was easily the best engine fitted to the Satellite. Other modifications made to the aircraft after the original Trials included a reduction of the wing span after the Cherub II had been installed. Eventually the Satellite was returned to Short Brothers where it remained, never again being flown.

Data
Power plant: See NOTES
Wing span: *(original)* 10.36 m (34 ft); *(after reduction)* 9.75 m (32 ft)
Wing area, gross: *(original)* 15.61 m² (168 sq ft)
Length overall: 7.24 m (23 ft 9 in)
Weight empty: 290 kg (640 lb)
Max t/o weight: 481 kg (1,060 lb)
Speed range: *(Cherub engine)* 32–63 knots (60–117 km/h; 37–73 mph)

Variant
S.4 Satellite. Single prototype designed for the Two-Seat Light Aeroplane Trials. Described above.

S.1 COCKLE

First flight: 7 November 1924

Type: Single-seat light sporting flying-boat
Notes and Structure: In 1924 Short Brothers built a small single-seat flying-boat to the order of Lebbaeus Hordern of Sydney, Australia, who wanted it for his sporting activities. This order had been doubly pleasing, for it had not only given the company a new aeroplane project at a time when it was most heavily committed to non-aviation pro-

duction programmes but had enabled Shorts to construct an all-metal hull on the principles already employed in the Silver Streak and Springbok.

By coincidence, about the time of the order the Air Ministry had requested bids for the construction of a large all-metal flying-boat hull to suit the Felixstowe F.5. The significance of these two events had not been missed by Oswald, who saw in the design and construction of Mr Hordern's

John Parker attempting in vain to lift the Cockle from the Medway in October 1924

diminutive craft an opportunity of testing his theories and methods of construction before delivery of the large hulls.

The Hordern flying-boat received the first type number issued by the company, S.1, while the F.5 metal hull project became S.2. The S.1, originally named Stellite, was a high-wing monoplane with its fabric-covered wings braced from the chine of the hull to just outside the mountings for the engines. The wing spars and bracing struts were fabricated from 50-ton steel, the remainder of the wing structure from duralumin. Full-span ailerons and wing-floats were fitted. The duralumin monocoque hull had a wide and flared planing surface and inwards-sloping sides which *Jane's* called 'marked tumble home'. Interestingly, the two steps on the hull were built as a separate structure to the main hull. The pilot's cockpit was well forward of the wings and the engines were set between the front to rear wing spars. The engines themselves, though initially to be two Bristol Cherubs of the type fitted to one of the winning aircraft of the 1923 Lympne Competitions, were 697 cc Blackburnes, as described in the entry on the Gnosspelius Gull. However, following launch of the diminutive flying-boat in September 1924, by which time its name had been changed to Cockle, these engines proved incapable of lifting the aircraft from the Medway. Eventually the

angle of wing incidence was increased and the flying-boat took off but there was barely sufficient power.

It is unlikely that with Hordern piloting the Cockle it would have ever taken off, and he refused it. After modifications to the fabric-covered vertical tail, the Cockle was delivered to Felixstowe for testing. Before leaving Rochester it was marked with roundels and was allocated military serial N193 in place of its civil registration *G-EBKA*. At Felixstowe it was tested between July 1925 and August 1926, thereafter returning to Shorts to have two Cherub II engines fitted before purchase by the Air Ministry.

Data
Power plant: See NOTES
Wing span: 10.97 m (36 ft)
Wing area, gross: 19.51 m² (210 sq ft)
Length overall: 7.52 m (24 ft 8 in)
Weight empty: *(Blackburne engines)* 369 kg (814 lb)
Max t/o weight: *(Blackburnes)* 482 kg (1,062 lb)
Max level speed: *(Blackburnes)* 59 knots (109 km/h; 68 mph)

Variant
S.1 Cockle. Single diminutive flying-boat, the first by Short Brothers with an all-metal hull.

S.7 MUSSEL I and II

First flight: (Mussel I) 6 April 1926

Type: Experimental aircraft configured as two-seat trainers
Notes and Structure: The Mussel has special significance to the story of Short Brothers, having gained its name from the farmhouse purchased for the Aero Club (Mussel Manor) at Shellbeach in 1909 by Frank McClean. It was also the aeroplane in which Eustace Short learned to fly (Mussel I) and the aircraft in which he died from a heart attack while landing (Mussel II) on 8 April 1932. In its own right, the Mussel was a well designed light aircraft of mostly metal construction, easy to handle and adaptable for various forms of landing gear.

The development of the original Mussel began in 1925, primarily as a test aircraft for Short-developed floats but also as a tandem two-seat dual-control trainer. One major factor in its design

was the availability of the small ADC Cirrus I four-cylinder inline engine, designed by a team headed by Major F. B. Halford. ADC (or Aircraft Disposal Company) had been formed in 1920 to take over the sale of unwanted RAF aircraft produced under contract during the 1914–18 war; it later undertook aircraft and engine design and construction, its 48.5 kW (65 hp) Cirrus I weighing only 122 kg (268 lb).

During the flying career of the Mussel I, which began in April 1926 and ended on 24 August 1928 when Eustace struck the mast of a barge while landing on the Medway and virtually wrote off the machine, it was flown with experimental twin floats and a taildragger wheeled landing gear. It was built of metal, with the exceptions of the spruce wing ribs and fabric covering to the wings and tail unit. In configuration it was a low-wing monoplane type, the wings being rigidly braced by two compression struts on either side from the fuselage top to points about one-third of the half span. The duralumin monocoque fuselage was of a type

Mussel I before its first flight on 6 April 1926, without civil markings

which, after exhaustive mechanical tests carried out by the firm and the Royal Aircraft Establishment at Farnborough, had been embodied in nearly all machines built by Shorts to the order of the British Air Ministry over the previous postwar years. The fuselage shell was of oval cross-section, in which a sheet duralumin skin was employed as part of the stress-resisting structure, the sheets being riveted to transversely arranged channel section formers of the same material. On the inside of the tube thus formed, V-section longitudinal stiffeners of duralumin were riveted to the skin at intervals around the circumference. In order to facilitate internal inspection and transportation, the fuselage was built in two sections. From early 1928 a Cirrus II engine of 62.5 kW (84 hp) was fitted to the Mussel, differing from the original installation by being cowled.

After the loss of the original Mussel, Short Brothers decided to construct a new and slightly modified aircraft as the Mussel II, to continue experimental work in connection with float design and other projects and for the enjoyment of Eustace. Although basically similar to the Mussel I, the Mussel II had wings of new aerofoil section incorporating Warren type ribs of duralumin tube construction. As before, fabric covered the wings except at the roots, where duralumin sheet provided a walkway. The ailerons were of duralumin and fabric. The fuselage had flatter sides than on Mussel I and the first engine fitted was a 67 kW (90 hp normal rating) Cirrus III that weighed 129 kg (285 lb), driving a Short patent metal propeller.

The new Mussel II was launched in May 1929 and was certificated in the following June. Starting with new twin floats, it was soon converted to landplane form and then back to a twin-float seaplane, but in 1930 it was fitted with the Short Amphibian Undercarriage. A long description of this amphibious gear appeared in the 1931 *Jane's* and the following description has been taken from this:

'In 1929 Short Bros produced an amphibian undercarriage consisting of a main central float, a retractable land undercarriage and a pair of wingtip floats.

The float is the normal Short duralumin type, with a single step. . . .

The landing wheels are fitted between a pair of rubber-sprung legs mounted on to a cantilever axle rotating in bearings fitted inside the main float. Streamline duralumin fairings encase the axle between the wheels and the float.

On the axle between the bearings is mounted a light alloy casting housing a worm and worm wheel. This casting floats on the axle and is free to slide in another light alloy casting riveted to the trough of the float. Suitable stops are provided in the worm wheel casing limiting the extreme travel of the wheels. The worm gear is operated by means of a sloping shaft, incorporated in which is a universal joint, carried into the pilot's cockpit, the final drive being by a chain and hand-wheel.

A water rudder of the usual form and coupled to the rudder-bar is hinged to the stern-post of the float. This rudder also serves as a steering tail-skid when the machine is used on land, and is free to move up and down against the action of a coil spring.'

In August the Mussel II received an engine change, when a de Havilland Gipsy II was fitted in place of the Cirrus III. This was not the final configuration of the Mussel II, for, after the death of Eustace, the aircraft continued in use, receiving first a strange single mainwheel and underwing skid landing gear and finally a single main float and underwing stabilising floats. The Mussel II was retired in 1934.

Data
Power plant: See NOTES
Wing span: *(Mussel I)* 10.97 m (36 ft);
(Mussel II) 11.37 m (37 ft 3½ in)
Wing area, gross: *(Mussel I)* 18.58 m² (200 sq ft);
(Mussel II) 19.88 m² (214 sq ft)
Length overall: *(Mussel I seaplane)* 7.32 m
(24 ft); *(Mussel II seaplane)* 7.62 m (25 ft)
Height overall: *(Mussel I)* 3.28 m (10 ft 9 in);
(Mussel II) 3.58 m (11 ft 9 in)
Weight empty: *(Mussel I seaplane)* 467 kg
(1,030 lb); *(Mussel II seaplane)* 481 kg (1,061 lb)
Max t/o weight: *(Mussel I seaplane)* 715 kg
(1,576 lb); *(Mussel II seaplane)* 744 kg (1,640 lb)
Max level speed: *(Mussel I landplane)* 75 knots
(140 km/h; 87 mph); *(Mussel II seaplane)*
89 knots (164 km/h; 102 mph)
Max rate of climb at s/l: *(Mussel I landplane and Mussel II seaplane)* 189 m (620 ft)/min
Endurance: *(Mussel II seaplane)* 4 h

The Mussel II with a Cirrus III engine and fitted with the Short Amphibian Undercarriage, flown in this configuration on 8 March 1930

Variants
Mussel I. Original version, flown between 6 April 1926 and 24 August 1928. Oval-section fuselage and wings with spruce ribs.
Mussel II. Later refined version, with duralumin wing ribs and flat-sided fuselage. Only version to be fitted with Short's Amphibian Undercarriage.
Additional notes: Full description of the Mussel II appears in the 1931 edition of *Jane's All the World's Aircraft.*

S.5 SINGAPORE, S.12 SINGAPORE II and S.19 SINGAPORE III

First flights: (S.5) 17 August 1926
(S.12) 27 March 1930
(S.19) 15 June 1934

Types: Long-range biplane flying-boats
Notes and Structure: In 1924 Short Brothers built a metal hull to suit the RAF's Felixstowe F.5 flying-boat and in January of the following year this was launched as the Short S.2 with F.5 wings, etc, fitted. The same year Short Brothers received an Air Ministry contract for a single prototype flying-boat with a metal hull to comply with official Specification 13/24. This became the S.5 Singapore, a twin Rolls-Royce Condor III-engined reconnaissance biplane with open accommodation for a crew of five, unequal-span biplane wings and a monoplane tail unit with a small auxiliary fin and rudder carried each side of the large central fin and rudder. The interior of the hull was fitted with bunks and equipment for the crew when engaged on long-distance flights or when operating with the Fleet.

The Singapore was flight tested by Shorts and the MAEE over many months and several important changes were made, the most visible of which was the removal of the auxiliary fins and rudders. Other changes included the adoption of 485 kW (650 hp) Condor IIIA engines. From 12 August 1927 the Singapore was one of four prototype flying-boats that took part in the RAF's Scandinavian cruise and it was thereafter lent by the Air Ministry for use on the Sir Charles Wakefield Flight of Survey Round Africa, led by Sir Alan Cobham, KBE, AFC. This lasted from 17 November 1927 until 4 June 1928.

The Singapore's wing structure was all metal, with fabric covering. The Condor engines, replaced after the Cobham flight by 634 kW (850 hp) Rolls-Royce H.10 (subsequently named

G-EBUP: Singapore I used by Sir Alan Cobham on the Sir Charles Wakefield Flight of Survey Round Africa

Buzzard) engines, were carried in streamlined nacelles midway between the wings. Radiators of long-tube type, with conical shutters, were mounted under the upper wing above the engines. Accommodation was provided for a gunner in the bow, equipped with a Lewis gun, bomb-sighting and release gear; the pilot and co-pilot in side-by-side seats aft of the bow cockpit, with dual controls; and the navigator, wireless operator and engineer in internal compartments. Aft of the rear spar frame were two more open Lewis gun positions, staggered on each side of the centre-line to give a wide angle of fire in all directions.

The original type of Singapore was not ordered into production. However, to Specification R.32/27 Shorts joined Blackburn, Supermarine and Saunders-Roe in designing a prototype. While the specification called for a triple-engined flying-boat, Shorts adopted a four-engine layout in tandem pairs for its Singapore II, each a Rolls-Royce F.XII. The 'F' type was the development version of what became the Kestrel, the engine having been designed with the object of producing an economical engine of low frontal area and light weight suitable for all military purposes.

The Singapore II was a straight development of

the original Singapore but during trials a number of problems emerged. Several improvements were introduced thereafter and the structure was cleaned up, partly as the result of tropical trials in Aden. Apart from the adoption of a triple fin and rudder tail unit, four production Kestrel engines replaced the F.XIIs, arranged as two Mk IIIMS types geared .477–1 and two Mk IIMS geared .552–1. Extended service trials eventually proved the Singapore II to be very satisfactory, and the aircraft was shown to be capable of maintaining height at full load on two engines only. In final configuration the Singapore II adopted an enclosed cockpit for the pilots and had a tail gun position.

Production of the Singapore as a reconnaissance and coastal patrol flying-boat for the RAF began with four pre-production aircraft, the first of which took to the air initially on 15 June 1934. These were used subsequently for training. Full production Singapore IIIs, of which thirty-three were built in batches, became operational from 1935, initially replacing Rangoons with No 203 Squadron. These served at home, in Singapore and the Middle East, and for a period in 1937 a number were based in Algeria to offer protection to British ships in the Mediterranean and in the straits of Gibraltar during the Spanish Civil War. On the outbreak of new hostilities in 1939, a small number still served with the RAF. These were later handed over to the Royal New Zealand Air Force, with whom they served until 1945.

The Singapore III was, like earlier Singapores, an unequal-span biplane, with the upper and lower centre-sections extending to the engine struts. Ailerons were fitted to both sets of wings. The two-step hull had a planing bottom specially designed to eliminate any tendency to porpoise and used the normal type of construction consisting of frames built to the shape of the hull, to which was attached the metal skin. Heavy spar frames were built into the hull in line with the wings and tail unit. The wingtip floats were of similar construction. The remodelled Singapore II's triple type tail unit was standard, the tracking centre fin controlled from the cockpit. Power was provided by two Kestrel IX engines in front and two Kestrel VIII engines at the rear, each rated at 544 kW (730 hp) maximum at 1,600 m (5,250 ft). Accommodation provided for a gunner/bomber's position in the nose cockpit. The enclosed pilots' compartment had side-by-side seating and complete dual controls (the co-pilot's seat and controls were detachable). A central gangway between the seats gave access to the front compartment. Aft of the flight compartment was the officers' quarters with two bunks. Between the spar frames was accommodation for the engineer and wireless operator. Aft of this was the crew's quarters with three bunks. Provision was made for cooking, stowage of drogues, dinghy, etc. A midship gun position aft of the wings had a sliding gun-mounting so that vertical fire could be undertaken on both sides of the hull. At the extreme aft end of the hull was the tail-gunner's cockpit. All three positions carried a Lewis gun and the aircraft could carry up to 907 kg (2,000 lb) of bombs.

The first of four initial Singapore IIIs for the RAF

Data

Power plant: See NOTES

Wing span: *(Singapore I)* 28.35 m (93 ft); *(Singapore II and III)* 27.43 m (90 ft)

Wing area: *(Singapore I)* 160.44 m² (1,727 sq ft); *(Singapore II)* 162.58 m² (1,750 sq ft); *(Singapore III)* 170.38 m² (1,834 sq ft)

Length overall: *(Singapore I)* 19.96 m (65 ft 6 in); *(Singapore II)* 19.43 m (63 ft 9 in); *(Singapore III)* 19.56 m (64 ft 2 in)

Height overall: *(Singapore I)* 6.40 m (21 ft); *(Singapore III)* 7.19 m (23 ft 7 in)

Weight empty: *(Singapore I)* 5,876 kg (12,955 lb) with Buzzard engines; *(Singapore II)* 8,137 kg (17,940 lb); *(Singapore III)* 8,355 kg (18,420 lb)

Military load: *(Singapore III)* 1,272 kg (2,805 lb)

Singapore II during trials in April 1930

Max t/o weight: *(Singapore I)* 9,072 kg
(20,000 lb) with Buzzard engines; *(Singapore II and III)* 14,288 kg (31,500 lb)
Max level speed: *(Singapore I)* 111 knots
(206 km/h; 128 mph); *(Singapore II)* 122 knots
(225 km/h; 140 mph); *(Singapore III)* 126 knots
(233 km/h; 145 mph)
Rate of climb at s/l: *(Singapore I)* 271 m
(890 ft)/min; *(Singapore III)* 213 m (700 ft)/min
Service ceiling: *(Singapore I)* 4,725 m (15,500 ft);
(Singapore III) 4,575 m (15,000 ft)
Range at cruising speed: *(Singapore I)* 782 nm
(1,448 km; 900 miles); *(Singapore II and III)*
868 nm (1,609 km; 1,000 miles)
Armament: see NOTES

Variants

S.5 Singapore I. Single prototype of 1926. Two
engines only. Used on Charles Wakefield's/Sir
Alan Cobham's Round Africa flight of 1927–28 as
civil registered G-EBUP.
S.12 Singapore II. Revision of Singapore design to
new specification. Four engines in tandem pairs.
S.19 Singapore III. Four pre-production and 33
full production aircraft for RAF service, with modifications as outlined under NOTES. Some later
served with RNZAF.

A Singapore III after years of service with the RAF

S.3b CHAMOIS

First flight: 14 March 1927

Type: Two-seat army co-operation biplane
Notes and Structure: By 1926 it had become clear
that the Springbok was not going to progress
beyond the prototype stage as a two-seat fighter.
The reasons for this were mainly three-fold: firstly,
the Air Ministry saw little use for a new two-seat
fighter given the nature of the RAF's operations
overseas; secondly, existing aircraft were not then
outmatched in performance and plenty were available to the service; and, finally, those in charge of
maintenance were against the force having to
acquire the new skills associated with metal
construction.

In 1926 the first Springbok II was sent back to
Short's Rochester works from Martlesham Heath
(the permanent service aerodrome some 5 miles
from Ipswich), where it underwent major altera-
tion. Short Brothers were not prepared to abandon
its lead in the construction of metal aeroplanes and
so decided to adapt the Springbok II prototype to
fulfil Air Ministry Specification 30/24 for a two-

seat army co-operation aircraft. For this role the
aircraft was even more suited and J7295 re-
emerged as the Chamois.

The Chamois benefitted from work being conducted on a metal aircraft for fleet use (the
Sturgeon) and had new wings and tail unit. The
main changes were concentrated in the wings, with
the completely revised upper wing using the RAF

Chamois at Lympne prior to making its maiden flight

32 thick aerofoil section, new box spars and Frise ailerons that did not extend to the wingtips. Both the upper and much smaller span and chord lower wings were marginally sweptback, the latter without ailerons fitted. The Springbok's open section between the upper wings was replaced by a new centre-section with a circular opening for the pilot, and the gravity fuel tanks were incorporated inside the thicker wing. All these refinements were aimed at reducing drag. The Chamois was also a single-bay biplane but, like the Springbok, had fabric covering the steel spars and duralumin ribs. The tail unit of revised shape was also fabric covered.

Having first flown in March 1927, the single Chamois prototype was officially tested at Martlesham Heath from April. Another rejection in terms of production, but Short Brothers was not to be put off further work on all- or mostly-metal aircraft.

Data
Power plant: One 298 kW (400 hp) Bristol Jupiter IV.
Wing span, upper: 13.74 m (45 ft 1 in)
Wing area, gross: 40.88 m² (440 sq ft)
Length overall: 9.17 m (30 ft 1 in)
Max t/o weight: 1,910 kg (4,210 lb)
Max level speed: 104 knots (193 km/h; 120 mph)

Variant
S.3b Chamois. Single prototype only, converted from first Springbok II prototype.

CRUSADER

First flight: 4 May 1927

Type: Single-seat racing seaplane
Notes and Structure: Few people have any real appreciation of the historical significance of the Schneider Trophy contests, originated by Frenchman Jacques Schneider in 1912. Schneider believed that by international competition the design and performance of seaplanes would be greatly enhanced, and to this end he sponsored a competition and presented a trophy.

The first contest was just one item in the 1913 Monaco Hydro-Aeroplane Meeting and was won by a Frenchman at an average speed considerably lower than could be demonstrated by the fastest landplanes. However the 1914 contest was won by Britain with a specially prepared Sopwith Tabloid, showing that a properly organised team effort could not only benefit performance but gain the manufacturer of the aircraft considerable publicity.

Because of the First World War the third contest was not held until 1919, but there was no winner. Italy won the next two contests; only Italian aircraft entered because of post-war financial stringencies on Britain, France and America. Apart from having to taxi before flight to prove seaworthiness and then fly several laps of a marked course to give an average speed, the rules stated that if any country won the contest three times in a row the trophy would be retained for good. Fortunately for the survival of the competition, Britain won the 1922 competition but the 1923 and following contest in 1925 were won by the Americans, the British Supermarine S.4 having crashed and Gloster III outmatched.

The 1926 competition was again won by Italy, by which time a great deal of international prestige rested on the contest. Though unwilling, the British government gave in to demands that an official British team be organised for the 1927 contest. A high-speed development programme was started thereafter, with pilots formed into a new RAF High Speed Flight. Money was made available for new aircraft and engines, using the stalwarts Supermarine and Gloster as airframe manufacturers and Napier to supply high-power examples of its Lion inline engine.

Already by this date major advances in airframe design and engine development had resulted from the Schneider Trophy contests and those with business interests in radial engines for military production aircraft were concerned that they would soon lose their markets if nothing was done to show that radial engines could compete with inlines. As a result the Air Ministry was requested to back also a boosted derivative of the very new Bristol Mercury radial engine as part of the British effort, the Mercury-engined racing seaplane programme being supervised by Lt Col W. A. Bristow.

The Crusader racing seaplane was designed by W. G. Carter under the aegis of Bristow and construction of the single example was contracted to Short Brothers, already the manufacturer of the floats for several earlier Schneider racing seaplanes. The Crusader was a small monoplane of braced low-wing type. The wings were of a curious planform, having their greatest chord about halfway from the root to the tip and were roughly elliptical beyond this greatest chord. Construction used spruce box spars and ribs, covered with mahogany veneer and doped silk. The circular-section fuselage was mainly a wooden monocoque

The Crusader racing seaplane, which afforded the pilot very limited forward vision but had incredible take-off performance

type, although from the cockpit to the engine mounting a steel-tube structure was employed. Two floats, previously assigned to Short Brothers for design and construction, were practically as long as the fuselage and made of duralumin (the starboard float being used also as a long-range fuel tank to supplement other tanks). These were exceedingly effective on the water and had surprisingly low drag. Similar floats were supplied for the Gloster IV racing biplane. The tail unit was cantilever, with fabric covering the moveable wooden surfaces and mahogany veneer covering the fin and tailplane. Power was provided by a highly developed Bristol Mercury radial engine of 716 kW (960 hp). This was an interesting engine as, in this specially boosted form, it represented the first use of the Mercury, whereas up to then the majority of racing engines were produced by tuning types already developed for service or commercial use.

The Crusader was extremely sturdy but, as the 1927 *Jane's* pointed out 'So far it is not claimed that a speed equal to that attained by racing machines with water-cooled engines has been attained'. Despite careful streamlining and individual helmeting to the engine cylinders, the Crusader was not equal to the Gloster IV or Supermarine S.5 with their cleaner inline engines. The Crusader was launched at Rochester on 18 April 1927 but did not fly for the first time until the following month at Felixstowe, where the High

Speed Flight was based. The pilot was H. J. L. Hinkler, a freelance airman who had previously flown the Gloster III and, historically, is best remembered for making the first solo flight from England to Australia, in February 1928. Pilots of the High Speed Flight thereafter flew the Crusader, which suffered continuously from engine-running problems resulting in several near misses. In August 1927 it was taken to Venice, venue for the Schneider Trophy contest, together with S.5s and a Gloster IVA. There it was re-engined with a full-power Mercury (previous engines fitted having been derated) but it was clearly the least competitive British aircraft and was assigned to be used for practice only. On 11 September the end of the line came for the Crusader when, while being piloted by H. Schofield, it went out of control soon after take-off and dived into the water. Schofield, badly shaken and bruised, was lucky to have survived. On examination it was clear that the accident had been caused by the ailerons being incorrectly rigged while in Venice.

The Crusader was, therefore, to take little credit for Britain's successful bid for the 1927 Schneider Trophy, which was won by Flt Lt Webster in a Supermarine S.5 (in second place was Flt Lt Worsley in the second S.5). Indeed, such had been the rapid progress in the advancement of racing seaplanes as a result of this competition that Webster's speed in the S.5 set a new world speed record for seaplanes and landplanes alike. The Crusader, while having a phenomenal take-off rate (ideal for racing aircraft), was the least successful of the three types of British racing aircraft and went some way in proving the superiority of inline engines over radials for high-speed fighters of the future.

Data
Power plant: See NOTES
Wing span: 8.08 m (26 ft 6 in)
Wing area, gross: 11.15 m² (120 sq ft)
Length overall: 7.62 m (25 ft)
Weight empty: 879 kg (1,938 lb)

Max t/o weight: 1,230 kg (2,712 lb)
Max level speed: 234 knots (435 km/h; 270 mph)
Note. The winning average speed of the S.5 in the 1927 Schneider Trophy contest was 244.6 knots (453.29 km/h; 281.66 mph), achieved on the power of a 671 kW (900 hp) Napier Lion VIIA engine.

Variant
Crusader. Single example, as described above.

S.6 STURGEON

First flight: 22 June 1927

Type: Three-seat reconnaissance biplane
Notes and Structure: In 1924 the Fairey IIID three-seat spotter-reconnaissance biplane began equipping the FAA and gave outstanding service for the remainder of the decade. The first specification issued in 1924 covered a likely future replacement for the IIID and both Short Brothers and Parnall had the unhappy prospect of trying to better a likely successor from Fairey. To Specification 1/24 Shorts designed its Sturgeon, another prototype with an all-metal monocoque fuselage, featuring also fabric covered unequal-span metal wings with upper and lower ailerons and powered by a 335.5 kW (450 hp) Bristol Jupiter VI radial engine. The crew of three were accommodated in tandem cockpits, the forward cockpit for the pilot, the central cockpit with dual controls for the navigator (who doubled as bomb-aimer when required), and the aft cockpit for the

The first Sturgeon on the Medway in 1927

wireless operator/gunner with a Lewis gun. Provision in the design allowed for either a wheeled or twin-float undercarriage to be fitted, although only the latter was flight tested.

The Air Ministry ordered two Sturgeons as N199 and N200, but these appeared some months apart. Parnall's Pike was an equal-span biplane with a similarly rated Napier Lion engine and could also use both forms of undercarriage. However, it is believed the Pike was tested on wheels, the two prototypes being N201 and N202. A Napier Lion was also the power plant for the single initial Fairey IIIF prototype N198, which flew before the Sturgeon (in March 1926). Such was the excellence of the IIIF that it subsequently went into large scale production for the RAF and FAA, with many hundreds serving over a long period and others being exported. The Sturgeon too, when officially tested, was found to possess excellent qualities and, although production aircraft were not ordered, the Air Ministry requested Short Brothers to bid for fleet fighter Specification O.22/26 on its strength, which eventually produced the Hawker Osprey for production.

Data
Power plant: See NOTES
Wing span: 14 m (45 ft 11 in)
Wing area, gross: 60.39 m² (650 sq ft)
Length overall: 9.91 m (32 ft 6 in)
Max t/o weight: 2,818 kg (6,213 lb)
Max level speed: 100 knots (185 km/h; 115 mph)
Armament: Fixed forward-firing Vickers machine gun, flexibly-mounted rear Lewis gun, plus light bomb load.

Variant
S.6 Sturgeon. Two prototypes built as S.710 and S.711. Described above.

S.8 CALCUTTA

First flight: 15 February 1928

Type: Three-engined commercial flying-boat
Notes and Structure: By 1926 Imperial Airways
had begun to find its niche as an international
airline, though European competition was
extremely fierce. The breakthrough for its long-
distance plans came with the arrival of the Armstrong Whitworth Argosy biplane, intended for
Imperial's trunk routes but initially used from July
1926 on the Croydon–Le Bourget service. Then
came the excellent de Havilland Hercules.

In the same year, 1926, two flying-boats were
ordered for Imperial Airways, the design of which
had been based on the Singapore reconnaissance
flying-boat then under construction at Short
Brothers. Like the new landplanes mentioned
above, the S.8 Calcuttas were triple engined, using
three Bristol Jupiters as adopted for the Hercules
(but of a later and more powerful model). Each
Calcutta had accommodation for fifteen passengers, as detailed below. The first of these was
G-EBVG, launched on 13 February 1928. This
was taken into Imperial's fleet on 26 July 1928,
and during the remainder of the summer from
early August it flew a Southampton–Guernsey
service.

Meanwhile, the second Calcutta, G-EBVH, had
first flown on 3 May and differed from the first in

**The first Calcutta, named *City of Alexandria* by Imperial
Airways**

having Handley Page automatic slots in the upper
wing. This flying-boat was delivered to Imperial in
September, and between the 28th of that month
and 4 October it flew a Liverpool–Belfast shuttle
to correspond with Liverpool's Civil Week. The
single fare for this route was £3.10 shillings and the
return £6.10 shillings. During the winter of
1928–29 the Southampton–Guernsey service was
reduced to one flight a week in each direction but,
having proved the competence and seaworthiness
of the Calcutta, was closed down at the end of
February 1929 in preparation for the Calcuttas'
greatest trial.

On 30 March 1929 Imperial Airways inaugurated a commercial mail and passenger service
from Croydon, England, to Karachi, India, via
Switzerland, Italy and Egypt. This service, which
took seven days, involved a flight by Argosy from
England to Basle (Switzerland), a train journey to
Genoa (Italy), Calcutta from Genoa to Alexandria
(Egypt), train from Alexandria to Cairo, and then
on to Karachi by Hercules. Therefore, the Calcutta
was first used on the service on 31 March, the
passengers having taken the first day to arrive in
Italy.

On 6 April 1929 a third Calcutta was flown as
G-AADN, featuring modifications to the tail unit.
The England–India service began well but in
October the Italian government stopped Imperial
from using Italy as a stopping point after a wrangle
over profit sharing with Italian services over the
Mediterranean. From this point Calcuttas flew
from Athens. However, at the end of October

G-AADN had been lost and a replacement ordered as G-AATZ, which first flew in May 1930. This was some four months after Imperial's fourth Calcutta had appeared as G-AASJ. Before the Italian government once again allowed Imperial use of Italian bases, in early 1931, Calcuttas helped to shorten the England–India route by flying passengers from Salonika (Greece) instead of Athens. For a period in 1931, while new Kents were out of use, the Calcuttas maintained the re-routed Mirabella (Spain)–Alexandria Mediterranean sector and their newly appointed Khartoum–Kisumu Nile stage of the England–Africa service, landing at Kisumu on Lake Victoria (Kenya). From October 1931 the Mirabella–Alexandria stage became part of the England–Africa route, operated by Calcuttas, leaving Kents to fly the India route from Italy. During their career Calcuttas also flew to Haifa.

Following the loss of G-AASJ on the last day of 1935, after it ran out of fuel on its approach to Alexandria, and the Calcutta's general lack of range over the sector, all three were handed over to Imperial's Air Service Training Ltd subsidiary at Hamble in 1936–37, as conversion trainers for C-class flying-boats. One, G-EBVG, received new 567 kW (760 hp) Armstrong Siddeley Tiger VI engines but was lost in a training flight to Mirabella in 1937. The last Calcutta was retired from flying in 1939. Apart from Imperial's Calcuttas, one more aircraft was supplied to the French government as F-AJDB, first flown in September 1929, and a further example followed for the French Navy via Bréguet a couple of years later to join four built by Bréguet in France. Bréguet's three-engined Bizerte of 1933, of which more than thirty served with the French Navy from 1935–40, was derived from the Calcutta, as was the civil French Saigon. There was also reportedly interest in the Calcutta from the Keystone Aircraft Corporation in the USA, but nothing came of this.

The Calcutta itself was an unequal-span biplane. The upper and lower wing centre-sections were interconnected by a series of struts which supported the three engine mountings. The lower wings were braced to the hull by parallel steel-tube struts and interplane struts connected the outer wing sections. The wing structure used two corrugated duralumin box spars; the spars were built up of laminations of duralumin. The ribs were of Warren girder type, constructed of duralumin tubing.

The two-step hull used its duralumin skin plating as the main stress-carrying member. The tail unit was monoplane type, with balanced rudder and elevators. Power was provided by three Jupiter engines. Accommodation provided for two pilots side-by-side in an open cockpit at the nose of the hull. The co-pilot also combined the roles of

Short-built S.8/2 Calcutta for the French government

navigator and wireless operator, having a compartment aft of the flight cockpit. The passenger cabin sat fifteen persons, with a buffet provided. Aft of this cabin was the toilet and then the baggage compartment. Interestingly, the metal-framed passenger seats were fitted with detachable kapok-filled cushions which doubled as emergency lifebelts.

Data

Accommodation: 15 passengers
Power plant: Three 403 kW (540 hp) Bristol Jupiter XIF geared radial engines. One Calcutta later fitted with Armstrong Siddeley Tiger VI of 567 kW (760 hp). French Calcuttas with Gnome-Rhône Jupiter 9Akx radials.
Wing span: 28.35 m (93 ft)
Wing area: 169.55 m² (1,825 sq ft)
Length overall: 20.12 m (66 ft)
Height overall: 5.94 m (19 ft 6 in)
Weight empty: 5,808 kg (12,804 lb)
Average payload, plus crew: 2,132 kg (4,700 lb)
Max normal weight: 10,206 kg (22,500 lb)
Max level speed: 107 knots (198 km/h; 123 mph)
Cruising speed: 84 knots (156 km/h; 97 mph)
Rate of climb at s/l: 216 m (710 ft)/min
Service ceiling: 3,810 m (12,500 ft)
Range: 564 nm (1,046 km; 650 miles)

Variants

S.8 Calcutta. Five flying-boats for Imperial Airways. Two lost in Imperial Airways' operations (Spezio and Alexandria). One Air Service Training Calcutta capsized (at Mirabella) and later scrapped.
S.8/2 Calcutta. One for French government and second to Bréguet to join French Navy. Increased fuel capacity in second aircraft, which first flew in June 1931.

S.10 GURNARD

First flight: (Gurnard II) April 1929

Type: Two-seat fleet fighter and reconnaissance biplane

Notes and Structure: Specification O.22/26 provided for the development of a new fleet fighter-reconnaissance aircraft to supersede the Flycatcher and Fairey IIIF which operated from aircraft carriers, off gun-turret platforms and from shore stations on wheel and float undercarriages. This was an attractive proposition and tenders were submitted by Short Brothers (the S.10 Gurnard, the two prototypes ordered by the Air Ministry being allocated serials N228 and N229), Blackburn (the Nautilus, N234), Hawker (Osprey, the first prototype being a converted Hart), and Fairey (Fleetwing, N235). All the prototypes, except for the first Gurnard, were powered by the Rolls-Royce Kestrel and were extremely streamline in appearance, none more so than the Fleetwing. With the 391.5 kW (525 hp) Kestrel fitted, the Short prototype was known as the Gurnard II (built as S.745). The Gurnard I (S.744) was less pleasing to the eye because of its 395 kW (530 hp) Bristol Jupiter X radial engine.

The Gurnard was a near equal-span biplane, with staggered wings of unequal chord. The wings were of the normal two-spar type, built mainly of duralumin, and were arranged to fold for stowage on board ship. Special slings were provided for hoisting the aircraft out of the water when required to do so. Frise type ailerons were fitted to the upper wing only. The fuselage was a welded steel-tube structure, covered mainly with fabric, although aluminium was used for the top decking. Large detachable panels were provided to give easy access to equipment. Catapult points were provided in the fuselage. The rear end of the fuselage was built as a duralumin monocoque, into which the cantilever tail control surfaces were

Gurnard II landplane. Note the different heights of the cockpits and the Lewis gun fitted to the rear cockpit

rigidly built. For tail adjustment the whole unit was hinged and could be rocked by hand-wheel in the pilot's cockpit to vary incidence. A cross-axle Vee wheeled undercarriage could be interchanged with a stainless steel float chassis with two long single-step duralumin floats. Each float had a water rudder operated by the rudder bar. For transportation and handling, the floats were designed to use detachable handling trolleys. Initially the Gurnard I used a Townend low-drag cowling ring round the engine. Accommodation was provided for two, the pilot's cockpit under a cut-out in the trailing-edge of the top wing and the observer's cockpit at a lower level immediately behind. Armament consisted of one fixed forward-firing Vickers gun in the top cowling and one Lewis gun for the observer.

The Jupiter-engined Gurnard I appeared in early May 1929, some time after the Gurnard II, configured as a landplane. It was first flown on 8 May at Lympne and, after initial trials at Martlesham Heath, underwent some changes. It reappeared in July but in early 1930 was tested at Felixstowe in seaplane configuration with the Townend cowling ring removed, improving its appearance. The more streamlined Gurnard II

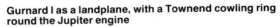

Gurnard I as a landplane, with a Townend cowling ring round the Jupiter engine

first appeared in April and, after its early flights from the Medway as a seaplane and revision of the ailerons, also went to Martlesham. Later the Gurnard II was tested as a landplane but in the event neither Gurnards could prevent production orders going to Hawker. The Gurnard II finished its days as a testbed aircraft at Felixstowe, having already flown with an amphibious undercarriage comprising a central main float, underwing stabilising floats and retracting wheels fitted to the main float. As for the Osprey, an initial order for 37 Mk Is with Kestrel IIMS engines was quickly followed by orders for examples with increased engine power, the Osprey Mk IV achieving 153 knots (283 km/h; 173 mph) in landplane form. Happily, Short Brothers was able to enjoy some of Hawker's success, receiving contracts to build floats for Osprey seaplanes.

Data
Power plant: See NOTES
Wing span: 11.28 m (37 ft)
Wing area, gross: 39.86 m² (429 sq ft)
Length overall: *(Gurnard I landplane)* 8.71 m (28 ft 7 in); *(Gurnard II landplane)* 8.84 m (29 ft); *(Gurnard I and II seaplane)* 9.60 m (31 ft 6 in); *(Gurnard II amphibian)* 9.91 m (32 ft 6 in)
Height overall: *(landplane)* 3.73 m (12 ft 3 in); *(seaplane)* 4.27 m (14 ft)
Weight empty: *(Gurnard I landplane)* 1,400 kg (3,086 lb); *(Gurnard I seaplane)* 1,581 kg (3,486 lb); *(Gurnard II landplane)* 1,479 kg (3,260 lb); *(Gurnard II seaplane)* 1,660 kg (3,660 lb)
Military load: *(Gurnard I landplane)* 399 kg (879 lb); *(Gurnard II landplane)* 395 kg (870 lb)
Max t/o weight: *(Gurnard I landplane)* 2,170 kg (4,785 lb); *(Gurnard I seaplane)* 2,352 kg (5,185 lb); *(Gurnard II landplane)* 2,175 kg (4,794 lb); *(Gurnard II seaplane)* 2,356 kg (5,194 lb)
Max level speed: *(Gurnard I landplane)* 145 knots (268 km/h; 167 mph); *(Gurnard I seaplane)* 134 knots (248 km/h; 154 mph); *(Gurnard II landplane)* 139 knots (257 km/h; 160 mph); *(Gurnard II seaplane)* 129 knots (240 km/h; 149 mph)
Climb to 4,575 m (15,000 ft): *(Gurnard II landplane)* 18 min; *(Gurnard II seaplane)* 19.6 min
Service ceiling: *(Gurnard II landplane)* 6,100 m (20,000 ft); *(Gurnard II seaplane)* 5,670 m (18,600 ft)
Endurance: 3½ h
Armament: See NOTES

Variants
S.10 Gurnard I. Single prototype with Bristol Jupiter X radial engine. Flown as landplane and seaplane.
S.10 Gurnard II. Single prototype with Rolls-Royce Kestrel II twelve-cylinder Vee engine. Flown as seaplane, landplane and amphibian.

Gurnard II amphibian in 1931, moored on the Medway with a Calcutta to its rear

S.11 VALETTA

First flight: 21 May 1930

Type: Three-engined 17-passenger transport monoplane

Notes and Structure: During the 1920s Short Brothers produced both seaplanes and flying-boats, each configuration having its own advantages and disadvantages for certain types of operation. However, the beauty of the seaplane was its easy conversion into landplane form to expand its possible areas of operation and therefore markets. Of course there were many operating advantages to the seaplane over the flying-boat, but on the whole these were mostly apparent in operations to and from inland water, as for sea work there was little to better the more rugged but heavier flying-boat.

Using the type number S.9, Short Brothers set about designing a single-engined passenger-carrying seaplane of modern form but, at the Air Ministry's request, this was modified into the three-engined S.11 to Specification 21/27 for comparison in operation with the Calcutta flying-boat (which was then being built by Shorts for service with Imperial Airways).

The resulting S.11 Valetta was a braced high-wing monoplane. The wings, with half-span narrow-chord ailerons inset from the tips but

otherwise of typical Short construction and fabric covered, were attached directly to the top of the fuselage and braced by struts on either side to the apex of a triangulated structure to which the floats were attached. The bracing structure consisted, on each side, a pair of parallel struts running out from the bottom of the fuselage (parallel to the wing) to a point immediately over the centre-line of the float. A further pair of struts ran down from the top of the fuselage.

The rectangular monocoque fuselage consisted of a number of duralumin frames, to which was riveted the outside skin and reinforced by longitudinal stiffeners. Strengthened frames were located in the region of the main spars and tailplane. The interior of the fuselage was, therefore, entirely free from obstruction. The two pilots were seated side by side in the flight compartment, with dual controls.

To the rear was a luggage compartment and wireless cabin. Then followed the main passenger cabin, 5.18 m (17 ft) long, 1.83 m (6 ft) high and 1.88 m (6 ft 2 in) wide, providing seating for the 17 passengers, mostly three abreast. Large opening windows were provided throughout the length of the cabin, and the cabin was sound-proofed. Aft of the cabin were the toilet and washing facilities. As for the Calcutta, the seats had cushions that doubled as lifebelts in an emergency. The tail unit of the Valetta comprised a braced tailplane with elevators, fin and balanced rudder, and a trailing servo rudder. Twin floats were provided, each with

Valetta gathering speed on the Medway for its maiden flight in seaplane configuration

Valetta landplane, seen at Croydon Airport where it was flown by pilots from Imperial Airways before ending its days at Martlesham Heath

a single step and constructed of duralumin. An alternative twin mainwheel land undercarriage was available, incorporating a special design of shock absorber gear, wheel brakes and a steerable tailwheel. The three engines, 403 kW (540 hp) Bristol Jupiter XI.F geared radials, were carried in the fuselage nose and in a nacelle under each wing.

Civil-registered G-AAJY, the one and only Valetta, made its maiden flight in May 1930 and was evaluated at Felixstowe between October that year and February 1931. Thereafter it was modified for a survey flight of the Nile region and the lakes of Central Africa, to be flown by Sir Alan Cobham and crew at the instruction of Imperial Airways, in preparation for a Cairo–Capetown service by the airline. In modified form it appeared at the beginning of July and on the 22nd the outward journey began. One of the five crew members under Cobham was Howard Bell, known as 'Dinger' and who, in 1909, had become the world's first apprentice to the industry by joining Short Brothers.

Lake Kivu, in what is now the east coast of Zaïre and some distance west of Lake Victoria, was reached on 8 August and the return journey began on the 14th and took the remainder of the month. It is a matter of aviation history that the first half of the proposed Cairo–Capetown route, from Cairo to Mwanza, was inaugurated by Imperial Airways in the summer of that year, with the second half to Capetown starting in December. The through-weekly service between England and South Africa was inaugurated on 20 January 1932, the journey initially taking 10½ days.

From December 1931 to early May 1932 the Valetta was not flown, but instead was fitted with the wheeled landing gear. In this form it took to the air again on 13 May but found no proper role thereafter. Following a brief period of service with the Air Ministry as a testbed, it was wrecked in the latter part of 1933. Interestingly, the Valetta had the greatest wing span of any Short monoplane flown from land, with the exception of the Sperrin jet.

Data
Accommodation: Two pilots and 17 passengers
Power plant: See NOTES
Wing span: 32.61 m (107 ft)
Wing area, gross: 128.39 m² (1,382 sq ft)
Length overall: 21.23 m (69 ft 8 in)
Height overall: (seaplane) 5.94 m (19 ft 6 in); (landplane) 4.72 m (15 ft 6 in)
Weight empty: (seaplane) 6,593 kg (14,535 lb); (landplane) 6,343 kg (13,985 lb)
Max t/o weight: (seaplane) 10,160 kg (22,400 lb); (landplane) 9,911 kg (21,850 lb)
Max level speed: (seaplane) 117 knots (217 km/h; 135 mph); (landplane) 120 knots (222 km/h; 138 mph)
Rate of climb at s/l: (seaplane) 259 m (850 ft)/min; (landplane) 268 m (880 ft)/min
Service ceiling: (seaplane) 4,265 m (14,000 ft); (landplane) 4,510 m (14,800 ft)
Range at cruising speed: (seaplane and landplane) 452 nm (837 km; 520 miles)

Variant
S.11 Valetta. Single example of a large 17-passenger seaplane airliner. Described above.

S.8/8 RANGOON

First flight: 24 September 1930

Type: Three-engined reconnaissance flying-boat
Notes and Structure: With No 203 Squadron based at Basra, Iraq (on the Persian Gulf) in urgent need of replacements for its Southampton II flying-boats, three military counterparts of the highly successful Calcutta flying-boat were ordered from Short Brothers for the RAF. Only the arrangement of the hull and the equipment carried varied from the civil aircraft, although fuel capacity was increased. The pilots were accommodated in an enclosed cockpit forward, and in the nose was an open position for a gunner with a Lewis gun on a Scarff ring. Aft of the biplane wings were two staggered gunners' cockpits, one on either side of the centre-line, again equipped with Lewis guns. The interior arrangement of the hull was very spacious and well ventilated, thanks largely to its civil ancestry, and was ideal for service in the Persian Gulf. All fuel was carried outside the hull, in tanks located in the top centre-section. Power plant remained three 403 kW (540 hp) Bristol Jupiter XIF geared radial engines.

All three Rangoons, as the military version of the Calcutta was named, were flown out to No 203 Squadron in 1931, each aircraft capable of carrying 454 kg (1,000 lb) of bombs under the lower wings if required. The aircraft performed very well and were well liked by their crews, as the result of

First Rangoon for service with No 203 Squadron, RAF

which two more Rangoons were ordered to official Specification R.19/31, differing in having stainless steel planing bottoms. The first of these made its maiden flight on 9 March 1932. One further Rangoon followed for No 203 Squadron, with an Alclad planing bottom, this last Rangoon first flying on 7 September 1934.

With the availability of production Singapore IIIs, No 203 Squadron handed five of its aircraft to No 210 Squadron at Pembroke, England, while the other went to Hamble as a trainer. However, after brief service in England and Gibraltar, this squadron too received Singapore IIIs and the five Rangoons were retired.

Data
Power plant: See NOTES
Wing span: 28.35 m (93 ft)
Wing area, gross: 169.83 m² (1,828 sq ft)
Length overall: 20.35 m (66 ft 9 in)
Height overall: 7.24 m (23 ft 9 in)
Weight empty: 6,350 kg (14,000 lb)
Max bomb load: 454 kg (1,000 lb)
Max t/o weight: 10,886 kg (24,000 lb)
Max level speed: 100 knots (185 km/h; 115 mph)
Service ceiling: 3,660 m (12,000 ft)
Range: 564 nm (1,046 km; 650 miles)
Armament: Three Lewis guns and up to 454 kg (1,000 lb) of bombs.

Variant
S.8/8 Rangoon. Six aircraft of three slightly differing types for RAF. Described above.

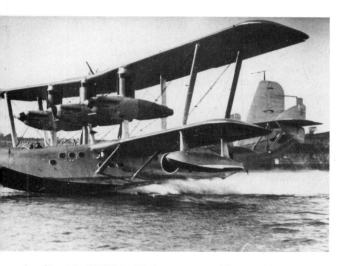

Short-built K.F.1 with Japanese markings, taking off from the Medway

S.15 K.F.1

First flight: 10 October 1930

Type: Three-engined long-range reconnaissance patrol flying-boat

Notes and Structure: In the early 1920s the Kawanishi Aeroplane Works was established as a division of Kawanishi Machine Works, having detached itself from the Japan Aviation Company owned by Mr C. Nakajima. In July 1924 the Kawanishi No 6 seaplane completed a round-Japan flight in nine days in the hands of Mr Y. Goto and the works became known thereafter for its seaplanes. In November 1928 Kawanishi Kokuki Kabusiki Kaisha (Kawanishi Aircraft Company Ltd) was formed to take over the aircraft works and wind tunnel of the Machine Works.

In 1929 Kawanishi was approached to build a new long-range flying-boat for the Imperial Japanese Navy. In view of Short Brothers' earlier association with flying-boats for Japan, Kawanishi sent its chief engineer to England, who was given official approval to inspect certain flying-boats recently completed by Shorts. As a result of negotiations with Short Brothers and Rolls-Royce, Short Brothers undertook to design a flying-boat for Kawanishi and provide a prototype, thereafter allowing all further construction to be the work of Kawanishi, while the Rolls-Royce Buzzard engine was to be licence-built in Japan.

The Short-built prototype was S.753, a three-engined biplane configured as an enlarged Rangoon with a Sarafand-type tail unit but with open crew cockpits. Carrying a crew of eight, it was defensively well armed, with gun positions in the bow, two midships and in the tail. Because of its

intended role, full sleeping and domestic accommodation was provided for the crew. Having completed its initial trials in England, this aircraft (carrying the serial M-2) was dismantled and sent to Japan, where it was erected by the Kawanishi company with the assistance of Short Brothers' personnel. Kawanishi thereafter built four similar flying-boats for the Navy as Type 90-2s at its new works at Naruo Mukogun Hyogoken, on the coast between Osaka and Kobe (occupied from the end of 1930), with Short personnel assisting but using Japanese labour and increasingly Japanese material. The first of these flew in March 1932 and were operated until 1936, each with a crew of six. The experience gained by the construction of Navy Type 90-2s gave Kawanishi the ability to develop (some years later) flying-boats used in the Second World War.

Data
Power plant: Three 597 kW (800 hp) Rolls-Royce Buzzard engines
Wing span: 31.05 m (101 ft 10 in)
Wing area, gross: 213.68 m² (2,300 sq ft)
Length overall: 22.68 m (74 ft 5 in)
Weight empty: 10,024 kg (22,100 lb)
Max t/o weight: 17,690 kg (39,000 lb)
Max level speed: 108 knots (200 km/h; 124 mph)
Max level speed: *(Type 90-2)* 119 knots (220 km/h; 135 mph)
Range: 1,737 nm (3,219 km; 2,000 miles)

Variants
S.15 K.F.1. Single prototype flying-boat to the order of Kawanishi of Japan.
Navy Type 90-2. Production version built in Japan by Kawanishi. Later designated H3K2. Differed in several minor respects to S.15, including having enclosed cockpit for pilots. Four built.

The third Navy Type 90-2 in service with the Imperial Japanese Navy at the Tateyama Air Station in 1933, a station that was home base for three of the Navy's 19½ aircraft squadrons

S.17 KENT and S.17/L

First flights: (Kent) 24 February 1931
(S.17/L) 26 March 1934

Types: Four-engined biplane flying-boat (Kent);
four-engined biplane airliner (S.17/L)

Notes and Structure: After Italian authorities denied Imperial Airways the use of its bases for the England–India route, ways were sought to overcome the problem and maintain the service. The initial solution has been detailed in the Calcutta entry but, to serve the Mirabella–Alexandria sector safely, Imperial required larger flying-boats to carry extra fuel. Indeed, one Calcutta lost in 1935 crashed as a result of running out of fuel en route to Alexandria. Another bonus of enlarged craft would be their ability to carry extra mail, which was a high revenue earner. Three flying-boats eventually emerged from Short Brothers for this service, subsequently known collectively as Kents but individually named *Scipio*, *Sylvanus* and *Satyrus*.

The Kents were based closely on the Calcutta but incorporated various improvements highlighted from the operation of the earlier aircraft. Apart from their four Bristol Jupiter XF.BM radial air-cooled engines mounted in tractor configuration to help cooling, each of which

S.17 Kent flying-boat *Sylvanus*, the second of the class launched at the end of March 1931

developed 414 kW (555 hp) at normal output at an altitude of 1,220 m (4,000 ft), the Kents were larger and the hulls were of more modern appearance. Accommodation was provided for two pilots in a new fully enclosed cockpit, behind which was the wireless operator's station. Immediately aft was the mail compartment and behind this the 15-passenger cabin. The passenger cabin had large windows, sound-insulated walls, good ventilation and lighting. A toilet and washing facilities were also provided for passengers and there was also a completely equipped steward's compartment. A large entrance hatch was provided over the rear luggage space for loading.

On 16 May 1931 *Satyrus* and *Scipio* inaugurated opposite-direction Kent services over the Mediterranean sector of the England–India route, but *Scipio* lost a float on arrival off Italy which put it out of commission for a few weeks. No sooner back in service, *Sylvanus* hit an Italian-operated flying-boat which again reduced the fleet while repairs were undertaken. However, these mishaps were soon forgotten as the Kents performed well over the newly negotiated Brindisi (Italy) stage to Haifa. For six months in 1932 Kents also flew mail services from Alexandria to Cyprus. A long period of successful operation followed, but in 1935 *Sylvanus* was destroyed by fire at the hands of an Italian and in the following year *Scipio* sank. *Satyrus* continued flying thereafter, from 1937 undertaking long-range survey flights for the airline. It was finally retired in 1938.

S.17/L *Scylla* taking on passengers

Meanwhile, in 1933 Imperial Airways required more large landplanes with which to maintain its services. In 1931 the airline had received its first giant Handley Page H.P.42 which, for European services in W (Western) form, accommodated 38 passengers. Others followed for European and Eastern routes but to the airline's request for two extra aircraft Handley Page offered monoplane derivatives for hand-over in 1935. Not struck with the radical idea, Imperial insisted on standard H.P.42s but the manufacturer quoted very high prices. Not able to go ahead with the purchase, Short Brothers were approached for the two landplanes.

To meet the quick delivery requirement, Short's airliner was based on the successful Kent flying-boat, the biplane wings, tail unit and power plant being identical. The fuselage, which had to be suitable for immediate requirements, became a semi-monocoque structure made up of lattice girders and built-up box longerons of duralumin, covered in corrugated Alclad skin. The interior was designed to equal the capacity of the H.P.42; seating was provided for 38 passengers, in a small smoking compartment of 2 m (6 ft 7 in) length and a main cabin divided into two sections of 6.65 m (21 ft 10 in) length. These cabins were 3.15 m (10 ft 4 in) and 3.28 m (10 ft 9 in) wide respectively, offering great comfort and space. The walls and interior doors were panelled with walnut.

The two aircraft were named *Scylla* and *Syrinx* and were completed and tested in time to begin European services to Paris and other cities by mid-1934. *Scylla* served Imperial Airways well and remained in commercial use in original form until the outbreak of the Second World War. After a brief period of military freighting and use on domestic services under BOAC, it was lost in April 1940. The end of *Scylla* was not the result of war-time action but of the weather, the aircraft having been overturned in a gale. A similar fate had attended *Syrinx* in late 1935, when at Brussels it had been overturned in a gale. However, on this occasion the damage was not severe enough to be beyond repair and it re-emerged ten months later with four 552 kW (740 hp) Pegasus XC engines, two having previously been fitted in place of the original centre Jupiter XF.BMs. This airliner was also retired in 1940. The S.17/L was the last civil biplane from Short Brothers.

Data
Accommodation: See NOTES
Power plant: See NOTES
Wing span: *(Kent and S.17/L)* 34.44 m (113 ft)
Wing area: *(Kent)* 245.26 m² (2,640 sq ft); *(S.17/L)* 242.94 m² (2,615 sq ft)
Length overall: *(Kent)* 23.90 m (78 ft 5 in); *(S.17/L)* 25.65 m (84 ft 2 in)
Height overall: *(Kent)* 8.53 m (28 ft); *(S.17/L)* 8.99 m (29 ft 6 in)
Weight empty: *(Kent)* 8,573 kg (18,900 lb); *(S.17/L)* 10,274 kg (22,650 lb)
Mail and other loads: *(not passengers, Kent)* 1,853 kg (4,085 lb)
Max t/o weight: *(Kent)* 14,515 kg (32,000 lb); *(S.17/L)* 15,195 kg (33,500 lb)
Max level speed: *(Kent and S.17/L)* 119 knots (220 km/h; 137 mph)
Cruising speed: *(Kent and S.17/L)* 91 knots (169 km/h; 105 mph)
Rate of climb at s/l: *(Kent)* 256 m (840 ft)/min
Absolute ceiling: *(Kent)* 5,945 m (19,500 ft)
Range at cruising speed: *(Kent)* 391 nm (724 km; 450 miles)

Variants
S.17 Kent. Three four-engined flying-boats, each accommodating 15 passengers.
S.17/L. Two four-engined landplanes, each accommodating 38 passengers.

S.14 SARAFAND

First flight: 30 June 1932

Type: Six-engined patrol and reconnaissance flying-boat

Notes and Structure: Although for most of the 1920s Short Brothers failed to win production orders for their aircraft designs, the experience of building prototypes plus producing Felixstowe F.3 and F.5 flying-boats under sub-contract helped greatly in the company's later success. Shorts' own venture into large flying-boats had begun, at Oswald's instigation, with the Cromarty. Commercial success came with the Calcutta and Singapore but Oswald had, for some years, been thinking in terms of very large flying-boats with transatlantic range. If Oswald required a final 'push', it came with the appearance in 1929 of the gargantuan German Dornier Do X. This monoplane flying-boat was capable of carrying 150 passengers and was powered by twelve engines supported on struts above the wing in six tandem pairs. Despite its pedigree and the world attention it attracted, it was not a success because of its poor hydrodynamic design and lack of power. The aircraft's subsequent flight in stages to the USA, between 2 November 1930 and 27 August 1931, was litle short of a fiasco and even two sister aircraft

At the time of its appearance, the Sarafand was the world's second largest aeroplane. This photograph was taken before 1934, when modifications were made to the hull

built for commercial use in Italy proved unsuited to either commercial or military operations.

If there was one thing that Short Brothers had learned from its years of research, it was how to design an efficient hull. Oswald therefore decided that Shorts should proceed with a project to build a huge flying-boat of its own, ostensibly however for long-range use with the RAF (probably considered the only likely user). Eventually Oswald managed to secure Air Ministry approval for the project, via the back door of Sir Hugh Trenchard who was then Chief of the Air Staff, and work on the flying-boat under official Specification R.6/28 began with part Air Ministry financing.

When the S.14 Sarafand appeared it was the world's second largest aeroplane, only the Do X being larger. However it was much more efficient, using only six engines but each of greater power than those on the German flying-boat. The Sarafand was an equal-span biplane, basically looking like a scaled-up Singapore. The upper wing was supported by struts from the engine nacelles and two pairs of vertical interplane struts. The lower wings were high mounted and, like the upper, used stainless steel spars and standard Short-type tubular duralumin ribs, the whole fabric covered. The two-step hull made good use of Alclad. The duralumin tail unit comprised a fin and rudder, braced tailplane and elevators and trimming fins on each side of the main fin. The rudder was balanced by set-back hinges and an

outboard trailing Flettner servo rudder. Power was provided by six Rolls-Royce Buzzard IIIMS twelve-cylinder Vee water-cooled engines installed in tandem pairs between the wings in monocoque nacelles, giving a total rating of 3,691 kW (4,950 hp).

Accommodation in the Sarafand was provided for ten. The bow cockpit could be fitted with either a 1½-pdr automatic gun or the more usual Lewis machine gun and included the bomb-aimer's position. The cockpit for the pilot and co-pilot seated in tandem was fully enclosed, under which ran a passage to the ward room. In this room were installed the wireless, navigator's chart board and the engineer's panels. A compartment positioned between the spar frames was suited to officers' quarters, where there was sufficient room for a removable table and four stowable bunk beds. Adjacent to this compartment was cooking and domestic equipment, thereafter the crew's quarters with folding bunk beds and a table. Aft of this was a further room with two bunks and stretcher stowage, provision for spare propellers and space to stow other items of equipment. A hatch in the roof allowed a spare engine to be lowered on to a supporting cradle for transportation. The aircraft's midship gun-rings were staggered, and to the rear of these were a toilet/washbasins and further areas for storing equipment. A walkway was provided to the rear gunner's position in the extreme tail.

The Sarafand was completed in 1932, but its huge size meant that it was launched on 15 June minus its upper wing and lower wingtips. Thereafter it was taken by river to a slipway for final assembly, where earlier Short barges had been built and launched. On the last day of June the Sarafand was flown and in July it was shown to the Press. Even though it flew well and met expectations, the RAF actually had little use for such an aircraft and so it was used for experimental work by the RAF until retirement. During its years of service, it demonstrated none of the vices of the Do X and so vindicated the concept of huge flying-boats with great engine power.

Data
Power plant: See NOTES
Wing span: 36.58 m (120 ft)
Wing area, gross: 321.44 m² (3,460 sq ft)
Length overall: 27.25 m (89 ft 5 in)
Height overall: *(on beaching chassis)* 10.21 m (33 ft 6 in)
Weight empty: 20,300 kg (44,753 lb)
Military payload: 2,708 kg (5,970 lb)
Max t/o weight: 31,750 kg (70,000 lb)
Max level speed: 133 knots (246 km/h; 153 mph)
Max rate of climb at s/l: 229 m (750 ft)/min
Service ceiling: 3,960 m (13,000 ft)
Range: 1,259 nm (2,334 km; 1,450 miles)
Armament: See NOTES

Variant
S.14 Sarafand. Single example, military serial S1589.

S.16 SCION

First flight: 18 August 1933

Type: Twin-engined light transport
Notes and Structure: From the outbreak of the First World War until the early 1930s virtually all landplanes built by Short Brothers were of a military nature, although there were exceptions. As the Rochester works had been developed mainly for the construction and testing of seaplanes and flying-boats, landplanes had to be disassembled for transportation to a suitable airfield before flight testing could begin. Therefore, when in 1933 the Rochester City Council decided to purchase land for an airport, Short Brothers became very interested in acquiring the necessary permission to build a hangar on the site.

Before Shorts established a facility at Rochester Airport, it had already begun work on a small feederliner accommodating five passengers. In this respect the resulting Scion broke ground for the type of aircraft that is, in the 1980s, the company's bread and butter. The prototype, initially named Alpha and later registered G-ACJI, was completed as a twin Pobjoy R-engined cantilever high-wing monoplane. The fabric-covered wing was built around a duralumin girder spar with duralumin ribs, and long narrow-chord ailerons were inset from a position near the wingtips. The fuselage was a rectangular structure of welded steel tubes, again covered with fabric, and fabric also covered the duralumin framework of the tail unit. Control surfaces for the latter were balanced on inset hinges. A divided-type undercarriage was used, each main unit comprising a long sprung leg, the top end of which was anchored to the front of the wing spar and the bottom hinged to the lower fuselage via steel-tube V-struts. Low pressure tyres were adopted and brakes fitted.

Scion prototype with the original flat fuselage decking, photographed during early flight trials at Gravesend

Accommodation was made for a pilot in the forward portion of the fully enclosed cabin, seated in front of the wing leading edge, while five seats were provided under the wing for passengers. An additional seat could be used, which folded. Controllable heating and ventilating systems were provided.

The prototype was taken by road to Gravesend Airport, where it made many flights. During the course of these early flights and demonstrations a curved top decking was added to the fuselage. On 16 December 1933 it was flown to the yet unopened Rochester Airport, even though Shorts' lease on land there did not start until 1934. It was, in fact, the first aeroplane to use Rochester Airport.

Meanwhile production of five aircraft had begun, each powered by two slightly more powerful 67 kW (90 hp) Pobjoy Niagara III seven-cylinder radial air-cooled engines. One of these (G-ACUW), with the prototype Scion (the adopted name after Alpha was dropped), was responsible for the nearest Short Brothers came to establishing an airline. Having been shown at the 1934 Farnborough air show, the Scions were used to demonstrate their many attributes as feederliners by flying a scheduled service between Rochester and Rochford Aerodrome, Southend,

in conjunction with Southend-on-Sea Flying Services. This lasted from 28 June to 26 October, during which John Parker and Harold Piper flew more than 1,000 services. Each passenger was charged 8 shillings for a one-way journey or 12 shillings for the return fare.

Scion G-ACUW was retained by Short Brothers until sold in April 1935 to Lundy and Atlantic Coast Air Lines of Devon. Two others of the production batch were sold to Aberdeen Airways and Papuan Concessions, the latter taken to Australia

Scion prototype with the new fuselage decking

The first Scion II G-ACUZ

as a twin-float seaplane. Of the remaining two Scions, one was retained by Shorts as a demonstrator and G-ACUZ appeared as the first Scion II.

The Scion II was basically a refined Scion with a few structural changes which included a moulded fuselage nose cone, additional equipment and an optional (proper) sixth seat. It was most easily identified from the Scion by its revised window layout, in which the pilot was provided with quarter lights in the roof and the side passenger windows were level with those of the pilot's windscreen.

G-ACUZ appeared in February 1935 and ten other production Scion IIs were built, three going to Australia. G-ACUZ was purchased by Airwork Ltd, while other British users of Scion IIs were

G-ACUX, the Scion seaplane for Papuan Concessions Ltd., later re-registered VH-UUP. This aircraft was still being flown three decades later, but as a landplane

West of Scotland Air Services, Southend-on-Sea Flying Services (who had been involved with Shorts' scheduled services in 1934), Olley Air Services and Pobjoy Airmotors. Of the remainder, Short Brothers retained G-ADDR and the city councils of Plymouth and Ramsgate acquired one each for the operation of short sight-seeing flights. The Short-retained Scion II was of particular interest, as it flew occasionally during its career with a plywood-covered scale wing of the Empire flying-boat for testing the configuration (designated M-3 by the company).

The original Pobjoy Airmotors company that supplied the Scion's engines had been founded by Douglas R. Pobjoy in 1930, but in 1935 it was made a public company with an authorised capital of £250,000. Because of the close work between Pobjoy and Oswald Short and Arthur Gouge representing Short Brothers (Rochester and Bedford) Ltd, Shorts purchased a major holding in the new company and both Oswald and Gouge joined the Board of Directors. The new company was renamed Pobjoy Airmotors and Aircraft in 1936, having acquired a licence to build the Scion. Thereafter the remaining new aircraft built were known as Pobjoy-Short Scions. A total of six Pobjoy-Short Scions was completed for sale, two of which went to Palestine Air Transport and one to Arabian Airways in Aden. Another was sent as a seaplane to Elders Colonial Airways operating in

Scion II VH-UVQ for Adelaide Airways in Australia

Sierra Leone, one went into private ownership, and the other to Lundy and Atlantic Coast Air Lines. Some Scions and Scion IIs changed hands but, between 1940 and 1941, no fewer than thirteen were taken into RAF service for wartime duties. A few remained flying into the 1960s.

Data

Accommodation: One pilot and five or six passengers
Power plant: See NOTES
Wing span: 12.80 m (42 ft)
Wing area, gross: 23.74 m² (255.5 sq ft)
Length overall: *(Scion)* 9.60 m (31 ft 6 in); *(Scion II)* 9.55 m (31 ft 4 in)
Height overall: 2.44 m (8 ft)
Weight empty, fully equipped, less W/T: *(Landplane)* 850 kg (1,875 lb); *(seaplane)* 964 kg (2,125 lb)
Pilot, passengers and baggage: *(landplane)* 479 kg (1,057 lb); *(seaplane)* 366 kg (807 lb)

Max t/o weight: *(landplane and seaplane)* 1,451 kg (3,200 lb)
Max level speed: *(landplane)* 111 knots (206 km/h; 128 mph); *(seaplane)* 106 knots (196 km/h; 122 mph)
Cruising speed: *(landplane)* 101 knots (187 km/h; 116 mph); *(seaplane)* 96 knots (178 km/h; 111 mph)
Rate of climb at s/l: *(landplane)* 191 m (625 ft)/min; *(seaplane)* 177 m (580 ft)/min
Service ceiling: *(landplane)* 3,960 m (13,000 ft); *(seaplane)* 3,505 m (11,500 ft)
Range: *(landplane)* 339 nm (628 km; 390 miles) standard tanks; *(seaplane)* 321 nm (595 km; 370 miles) standard tanks

Variants

S.16 Scion. Initial version with five standard passenger seats.
S.16 Scion II. Refined version of Scion with five or six standard passenger seats.
Pobjoy-Short Scion. Version of Scion II built under licence by Pobjoy Airmotors and Aircraft Ltd of Rochester

S.18 KNUCKLEDUSTER

First flight: 30 November 1933

Type: Twin-engined open-sea general purpose and reconnaissance flying-boat
Notes and Structure: In 1931 a new specification was issued which called for a twin-engined flying-boat capable of long-range patrols with the RAF (Specification R.24/31). Three British companies had the experience to meet such a specification and the Air Ministry ordered a single prototype from

each as the Short R.24/31 (later named Knuckleduster and carrying serial K3574), Saro A.27 and Supermarine Stranraer.

The A.27 and Stranraer were both unequal-span biplanes, their bottom wings mounted high on the hull and the upper carrying Bristol Pegasus nine-cylinder radial engines in the leading edges. Both adopted strut-braced tailplanes and twin fins and rudders. Short Brothers, however, decided to break new ground and the Knuckleduster became the company's first large monoplane flying-boat. Its most striking feature was its gull wings; from the roots to the engine nacelles it had 30 degrees of dihedral and the outer sections were horizontal but tapered in both chord and thickness. The wings were cantilevered and so were free from drag-inducing struts. The wing structure was built around a main spar constructed in the form of a braced rectangular tube. Four longitudinal booms were screwed at each end into sockets of similar material. The diameter and gauges of the tubes were reduced towards the wingtips, as loads became smaller, and finally terminated in pyramidal tubular frames to which the wing-end tubes were fitted. The wing ribs were built-up of duralumin, with tie-plates of similar material. The leading and trailing-edges of the wings were covered with metal sheet, the remainder of the wings being fabric covered. Frise type ailerons were used.

The hull was of flat-sided two-step type. The framework consisted of a deep 'I' central keelson, two smaller 'I'-section side keelsons and a number of transverse frames into which a complete set of bracing was built from bow to aft of the rear step. This braced structure was stressed to carry all the main loads, and stressed skin was additional to the main strength. Light intercostal 'Z'-section stringers between the frames supported the skin. The bottom surface was longitudinally plated with flat sheets, the side and top with corrugated sheets, all the Alclad. The wingtip floats had Alclad frames, keelsons, stiffeners, stringers and skin. The fabric-covered tail unit had a strut-braced tail-plane with elevators.

Power for the Knuckleduster was provided by two 578 kW (775 hp) Rolls-Royce Goshawk VIII twelve-cylinder Vee steam-cooled engines, carried on welded steel-tube mountings raised slightly above the wings at the 'knuckles'. Two main fuel tanks of 178 Imperial gallons capacity each and two 46 gallon gravity tanks were carried in the sloping portions of the wings. Accommodation was provided for a crew of five. In the bow was the first gunner's cockpit with bomb-aimer's hatch and seat. The pilots' cockpit (fully enclosed) was to its rear, the pilot himself on a seat to the port side, with removable dual controls on the starboard side; the navigator's compartment (with chart table and compass ports) also had two officers' bunks. The wireless operator's and engineer's room was between the spar frames, with both crew members facing forward. The crew's quarters, comprising two fixed bunks and one folding bunk, washing and cooking facilities, was aft of the engineer's compartment, behind which was in turn the midships gun cockpit, engineer's bench, drogue stowage, toilet and screened tail-gun cockpit.

The Knuckleduster was launched on 29 November 1933 and made its maiden flight the following day. Test flights revealed certain weaknesses in the tail unit and float struts but these were overcome and in mid-1934 the flying-boat was sent to Felixstowe for initial service trials. In March of the following year it was evaluated at Calshot and thereafter returned to Felixstowe, where it was flown until 1938. The Knuckleduster finished its days as an instructional airframe. Meanwhile, both the Saro and Supermarine flying-boats had received production contracts, the A.27 becoming the Pegasus III- or X-engined London which entered Coastal Command service from 1936, and the Stranraer with Pegasus X engines joined Coastal Command the same year.

Taking off from the Medway, the Knuckleduster fitted with larger rudders and the first type of sprung wingtip floats

Data
Power plant: See NOTES
Wing span: 27.43 m (90 ft)
Wing area, gross: 106.56 m² (1,147 sq ft)
Length overall: 19.28 m (63 ft 3 in)
Height overall: 6.10 m (20 ft)
Height on beaching trolley: 6.86 m (22 ft 6 in)
Weight empty: *(with water)* 5,316 kg (11,720 lb)
Military load: 1,581 kg (3,485 lb)
Max t/o weight: 8,391 kg (18,500 lb)
Max level speed: 130 knots (241 km/h; 150 mph) at 1,370 m (4,500 ft)
Cruising speed: 100 knots (185 km/h; 115 mph) at 610 m (2,000 ft)
Rate of climb at s/l: 244 m (800 ft)/min
Rate of climb at 915 m (3,000 ft): 213 m (700 ft)/min

Service ceiling: 4,450 m (14,500 ft)
Absolute ceiling: 5,030 m (16,500 ft)
Range at economical cruising speed: 850 nm (1,575 km; 979 miles)
Armament: One Lewis gun in each gun cockpit, the midships gun mounted on traverse rails for firing either side. Bomb load of two 500 lb or four 250 lb bombs, together with four light series and four reconnaissance flares. Provision was made for transporting one 18-in torpedo under starboard wingroot against hull.

Variant
S.18 Knuckleduster. Single prototype to Air Ministry specification, built as S.767. As described above.

S.22 SCION SENIOR

First flight: 22 October 1935

Type: Four-engined transport
Notes and Structure: Having built the twin-engined Scion, it became obvious that busier feeder services would require an aircraft of greater passenger capacity. Short Brothers was not alone in this assumption. De Havilland, having launched its D.H.84 Dragon six-passenger biplane with orders from Hillman's Airways, designed a ten-passenger four-engined larger derivative as the D.H.86, which flew in January 1934.

Shorts' larger Scion became the Scion Senior, a ten-passenger monoplane powered by four Pobjoy Niagara III engines and featuring a new tapering

First Scion Senior, delivered as a seaplane to Rangoon in early 1936

wing with rounded tips. Accommodation provided for the pilot in the forward cabin, a sliding door thereafter leading to the main cabin which was divided into two by a toilet on the starboard side. Each compartment had five forward-facing seats, and a baggage compartment was provided aft of the cabin.

Short Brothers designed the Scion Senior with a divided-type wheeled undercarriage, with long Vickers oleo-pneumatic shock-absorbing legs attached in a similar way to those on the smaller Scion. In this configuration it did not attract orders and so Short Brothers reverted to what it knew best and modified the design into a twin-float seaplane with optional land gear. In this form a single aircraft was ordered by Irrawaddy Flotilla and Airways Ltd of Burma, which, in November 1934, had inaugurated an experimental weekly service between Rangoon and Moulmein, extending it in January of the following year to Tavoy, some 232 nm (430 km; 267 miles) from Rangoon. A weekly service was also run from Rangoon to Mandalay, via Henzada, Prome, Yenang-Yaung, Chauk and Pakokku. The services had been initiated with a de Havilland Fox Moth but this had accommodation for just four passengers in addition to the pilot.

The first Scion Senior initially flew in the autumn of 1935. In January of the following year it was delivered to Rangoon as VT-AGU and, such was its success, a second Scion Senior followed in August the same year. Just four other Scion Seniors were built.

Although Pobjoy Airmotors and Aircraft received a licence to build the Scion Senior, all came from Shorts. The first of these was the land-

G-AECU, the only landplane version of the Scion Senior, first used as a company transport and demonstrator by Shorts

plane G-AECU, used as a company aircraft by Short Brothers from 1936 to 1938, thereafter going in turn to Jersey Airways, Palestine Air Transport (a Scion operator) and the RAF as a wartime impressed aircraft. The second Scion Senior of the group, G-AENX, was sold to an existing Scion operator and then passed to other Scion operators, West of Scotland Air Services and Elders Colonial Airways respectively. Another Scion Senior went to Burma, but the last became the most unusual seaplane of the series. This aircraft, allocated registration G-AETH but not taken up, was purchased by the Air Ministry as L9786. Not flown until October 1939, it featured a central float configured as a scale model of the

Short Sunderland military flying-boat hull and underwing stabilising floats on long struts. Used for experimental work, it sank in 1944.

Data
Accommodation: Pilot and ten passengers
Power plant: Four 67 kW (90 hp) Pobjoy Niagara III seven-cylinder radial engines
Wing span: 16.76 m (55 ft)
Wing area, gross: 37.16 m² (400 sq ft)
Length overall: 12.80 m (42 ft)
Height overall: *(landplane)* 3.00 m (9 ft 10 in); *(seaplane on trolley)* 3.66 m (12 ft)
Weight empty, equipped: *(landplane)* 1,657 kg (3,652 lb); *(seaplane)* 1,841 kg (4,058 lb)
Payload plus pilot: *(landplane)* 707 kg (1,559 lb); *(seaplane)* 523 kg (1,153 lb)
Max t/o weight: *(landplane and seaplane)* 2,608 kg (5,750 lb)
Max level speed: *(landplane)* 126 knots (233 km/h; 145 mph); *(seaplane)* 117 knots (217 km/h; 135 mph)
Cruising speed: *(landplane)* 109 knots (203 km/h; 126 mph); *(seaplane)* 104 knots (193 km/h; 120 mph)
Rate of climb at s/l: *(landplane)* 244 m (800 ft)/min; *(seaplane)* 187 m (615 ft)/min
Service ceiling: *(landplane)* 3,960 m (13,000 ft); *(seaplane)* 3,050 m (10,000 ft)
Range at cruising speed: *(landplane)* 365 nm (676 km; 420 miles) with standard tanks; *(seaplane)* 347 nm (644 km; 400 miles) with standard tanks

Variant
S.22 Scion Senior. Four-engined transport, as described above. Six examples only.

L9786, the Air Ministry's Scion Senior with a scale Sunderland-type planing bottom to the central main float *(Air Ministry)*

S.23, S.30 and S.33 C-CLASS EMPIRE FLYING-BOATS

First flight: 3 July 1936

Type: Four-engined commercial flying-boats

Notes and Structure: In 1924 Imperial Airways was formed as the first British national airline. This was at a time when the British share of European air traffic was declining; in 1924, for example, 6,616 passengers had flown between Britain and France on British aircraft compared to 5,919 on French. By the following year the figures were 6,547 and 7,753 respectively and even worse were the figures for mail, newspapers and other goods. The overall British percentage of air traffic across the Channel between Britain and France, Holland, Germany and Belgium fell from 57.6% for passengers in 1924 to 51.1% in 1925.

Gradually Imperial Airways established long-range routes to the British Empire, using landplanes, flying-boats and railways to link the stages through countries. Although competition remained high on European routes, Imperial's long-range services remained virtually unchallenged for some years. Therefore, while much improved aircraft were introduced on to its routes, Imperial saw little reason to rethink its use of trains despite the resulting inconvenience of transferring passengers and goods between aircraft and land transportation systems at various stages. However, as the early 1930s unfolded this situation became a matter for concern for several reasons, not least because American aircraft manufacturers were building new generation landplanes and flying-boats with monoplane wings that had performances far in excess of Imperial's biplanes. These, in the hands of rival airlines, were part responsible for taking traffic from the British carrier.

A demonstration of what Imperial could achieve with the right aircraft came from the RAF, which was then operating flying-boats successfully in Africa and from India to such destinations as Singapore and even Australia. The decision was therefore taken in 1934 to purchase for Imperial suitable new-generation flying-boats for use on all main Empire routes: flying-boats were chosen as they could be heavily loaded, large in size and high in performance without the need to modify existing airfields, as would be the case with landplanes. Extra size meant improved standards of luxury for passengers and the space needed to carry plenty of mail. The latter was an important consideration as, in 1935, the British government decided to price all mail within the Empire at ordinary surface rate. Short Brothers was asked to propose a design.

The original type of Empire flying-boat, to use the popular name although Imperial Airways knew the class as Imperial Flying Boats, had the Short type number S.23. This was designed to accommodate twenty-four passengers and baggage, together with 1½ tons of mail. Bunks and bedding were carried so that at any port it would be possible for the steward to refit the cabins for night flying with sleeping accommodation for 16 passengers. The aircraft's high-wing two deck layout possessed many aerodynamic and structural advantages. Unlike on the Knuckleduster, the high position of the wings gave sufficient propeller clearance without having to resort to a 'knuckle' wing or having to mount the four 685.6 kW (920 hp) Bristol Pegasus X.C nine-cylinder radial engines on struts from the hull.

S.23 *Canopus*, **the first of the famous Empire flying-boats**

S.23 *Clio* fitted with temporary beaching wheels, being crane-lifted back onto land at Queen's Island in 1940

In the extreme nose was a mooring compartment, aft of which was a lower deck smoking cabin with settees for seven persons and the buffet and toilets. To the rear of the buffet was the midship cabin, then the promenade cabin and aft cabin. A baggage compartment was situated to the rear of the aft cabin. On the upper deck was the pilots' cockpit accommodating the pilot and co-pilot, wireless operator, navigator and engineer. Also on the upper deck were the mail compartment and a room for stowing the night sleeping equipment when not in use. Like the wings (incorporating Gouge-designed dragless flaps which, when open, provided increased wing area in addition to the usual flap effect but when closed formed an almost continuous surface with the main wing), the two-step hull was of all-metal construction. Only the aircraft's Frise-type ailerons and the majority of the tail unit were fabric covered.

Short Brothers received an order that was gradually increased to 28 aircraft for Imperial Airways, placed 'off the drawing board' and without first requiring the construction and flight testing of a prototype. This was a massive order for the period, costing £1,750,000. A high proportion of the initial purchase price was to be offset by high revenue from mail carrying and, indeed, eventually Empire flying-boats were each limited to 17 daytime passengers so as to allow an increase of mail to 2 tons (the extra mail stowed in the smoking compartment).

Even before the first S.23 had been completed, some members of Parliament voiced openly in the House of Commons that these British aircraft could not possibly compare with the latest types appearing in America and elsewhere. Luckily few took notice of these persons, who had little reason for such comment. The first S.23 was launched on 2 July 1936 and the following day John Parker took G-ADHL *Canopus* on its first flight, lasting 14 minutes. All subsequent flying-boats of the C-class had names beginning with the letter 'C'. Of course these were not the first Short flying-boats to serve with Imperial Airways, smaller Calcutta and Kent biplanes having already given years of successful service.

Canopus recorded the first scheduled flight of the Empire type on 30 October 1936, on the trans-Mediterranean Alexandria–Brindisi route. The second Empire flying-boat to take to the air was *Caledonia*, on 11 September 1936. This was one of two aircraft to be provided with special fuel tanks (the other *Cambria*) for a range of 2,865 nm (5,310 km; 3,300 miles) and was used on a series of experimental transatlantic crossings in connection with the proposed North Atlantic service to be operated jointly by Imperial Airways and Pan American Airways. However, it was first used to transport Christmas mail in stages to India, carrying 5½ tons each way. The two long-range S-23s completed five scheduled transatlantic return trips during the summer of 1937. The first was made by *Caledonia* between Foynes, Ireland, and Botwood, Newfoundland, on 5–6 July, taking 15 hours 9 minutes for the journey. Having reached Botwood, the route continued to New York via Montreal. *Cambria* followed on 29–30 July but took 17 hours 48 minutes. The fastest time was by *Cambria* on the final west–east crossing, taking just 10 hours 33 minutes from 27 September and averaging 165 knots (306 km/h; 190 mph) (all ten times and dates are given in the 1937 edition of *Jane's*). A third flying-boat fitted (after early Mediterranean service) with special tanks was *Cavalier*, used on the Bermuda–New York service in conjunction with Pan American from June 1937 until early 1939.

Between 3 and 27 December 1937 *Centauras* made the first flying-boat survey flight from the UK to Australia and New Zealand, while earlier, in October, *Calypso* had inaugurated a scheduled service from Alexandria to Karachi. By 1938 no fewer than seven services each week were being flown to Egypt by Empire flying-boats, plus four to India, three to East Africa and two each to Australia, Malaya and South Africa. This period was the heyday of British flying-boats in commercial service. Earlier, on 5 March 1937, the new Imperial Airways flying-boat base at Hythe had been opened officially, marking the end of Croydon Airport as the centre of Empire services. However a number of Empire flying-boats were lost in the first two years of service, the first of which was *Capricornus*. This aircraft crashed in the

S.23 *Coriolanus* was built for Imperial Airways but was one of six Empire flying-boats operated by Qantas. It became the very last Empire flying-boat in service, retired on 8 January 1948, by which time it had flown more than 2,523,000 miles

French Alps during a snow storm on 24 March 1937, while on the first through mail service to Australia. An interesting, and little known, aspect of the accident was that the flying-boat was carrying a secret consignment of gold bullion worth £10,000, which was subsequently recovered.

Apart from the 28 C-class flying-boats ordered for Imperial Airways, the Australian airline Qantas ordered three, which were the last S.23s built. This airline also received other S.23s transferred from the Imperial fleet. The very last S.23 was G-AFBL *Cooee*, which became VH-ABF with Qantas. On 5 July 1938 Qantas inaugurated its C-class services on the Australia–UK route, with the initial service flown by *Cooee* from Rose Bay, Sydney. On 28 July the UK Empire Air Mail Programme was extended to Australia, New Zealand and a number of destinations in the Pacific, inaugurated by Imperial's *Calypso*, and on 2 August Qantas C-class *Carpentaria* left Sydney with the first airmail carried from Australia under the Programme. However, the first official airmail flight of this service was made two days later by Imperial's *Camilla*. The last S.23 Empire flying-boats were scrapped in 1947.

Although *Cavalier* had been used on the New York–Bermuda service, flown by Imperial Airways in conjunction with Pan American, the intended C-class flying-boat for this route was the modified S.30 Empire. The S.30 was generally similar to the S.23 except for using four 671 kW (900 hp) Bristol Perseus XIIC sleeve-valve

engines. Its structure was strengthened to permit a full C of A loaded weight of 20,865 kg (46,000 lb) initially, later raised to 21,772 kg (48,000 lb), and to allow air refuelling to a maximum weight of 24,040 kg (53,000 lb).

The first S.30 was *Champion*, initially flown on 28 September 1938 but without flight refuelling capability. This aircraft was fitted with 753 kW (1,010 hp) Pegasus XXII engines after the Second World War began. *Cabot*, *Clyde*, *Caribou* and *Connemara* had flight refuelling capability and were Imperial 'boats. The latter was destroyed in a fire in June 1939 and was replaced by *Cathay*. On 5 August 1939 a short-lived weekly transatlantic service was started between Hythe and New York, with refuelling taking place on the Foynes–Botwood section. S.30s could offer the same accommodation as S.23s but twice the range. Tanker aircraft for the 15 refuellings during 16 transatlantic crossings were Handley Page Harrow II bombers.

Three of the S.30s built were intended for trans-Tasman service with Tasman-Empire Airways Ltd (TEAL), an airline founded jointly by Britain, Australia and New Zealand. However, only two were delivered (without refuelling capability), the intended first having been involved in an accident in Basra and was later repaired as Imperial's *Clare*. In November 1939 Imperial Airways and British Airways merged into BOAC and it was a subsidiary of this new airline, known as Airways (Atlantic) Ltd, that maintained a transatlantic service with *Clare* during August and September 1940, without flight refuelling but taking off at the full 24,040 kg (53,000 lb) loaded weight. This same BOAC flying-boat inaugurated a wartime UK–Cairo service routed via Lisbon, Gibraltar and Malta in October 1941. Meanwhile, Tasman-Empire Airways had inaugurated a weekly air service between Auckland and Sydney on 30 April 1940, the first flight with *Aotearoa*.

Champion, the first S.30 version of the Empire flying-boat, first flown on 28 September 1938

Clio was impressed by the RAF as S.23/M AX659. The Boulton-Paul tail and dorsal turrets are clearly visible

The last of the Empire flying-boats were *Clifton* and *Cleopatra*, both of the new S.33 model. A third was cancelled. These were basically replacement aircraft for those lost in accidents while serving with Imperial Airways and had S.30-type strengthened hulls and Pegasus engines (finally Pegasus 22s) but were not capable of flight refuelling.

During the Second World War, many of the surviving Empire flying-boats were used on long routes all over the world. Two S.30s were the first to be taken over for military service with the RAF, thereafter being fitted with radar and armed for long-range patrols off the Scottish coast. Having later been converted back into transports, they flew to Norway but were destroyed by German aircraft. Two S.23 replacements were acquired as S.23/Ms, again installed with radar but also supporting gun turrets and packing depth charges. Most Empire flying-boats operated as transports during the war were re-engined with Pegasus 22s (as used by the Sunderland) and were responsible for many notable achievements. They flew schedules on the North Atlantic, the hazardous Mediterranean routes, and between Britain and Africa. Also, from 19 June 1940 until Japan entered the war, Empire flying-boats flew the so-called Horseshoe route linking Durban, Cairo and Australia, made necessary by the earlier severance of trans-Mediterranean services. Meantime, on 21 September 1939, two of Imperial's flying-boats that were in Sydney when war was declared were handed over to the RAAF. Two Qantas aircraft were thereafter taken over by Imperial Airways.

Data
Accommodation: See NOTES
Power plant: See NOTES
Wing span: 34.75 m (114 ft)
Wing area, gross: 139.35 m² (1,500 sq ft)
Length overall: 26.84 m (88 ft)

Height overall: 9.70 m (31 ft 9¾ in)
Weight empty: *(S.23)* 10,659 kg (23,500 lb); *(S.30 and S.33)* 12,330 kg (27,180 lb)
Payload plus 5 crew: *(S.23)* 3,629 kg (8,000 lb)
Payload plus crew: *(S.30)* 2,835 kg (6,250 lb); *(S.30 with flight refuelling)* 1,938 kg (4,270 lb)
Max t/o weight: *(S.23)* 18,370 kg (40,500 lb); *(S.30)* 20,865 kg (46,000 lb) later 21,772 kg (48,000 lb)
Max weight: *(S.30 with flight refuelling)* 24,040 kg (53,000 lb)
Max t/o weight: *(S.33)* 24,040 kg (53,000 lb)
Max level speed: 174 knots (322 km/h; 200 mph)
Max cruising speed: 142 knots (264 km/h; 164 mph)
Rate of climb at s/l: *(S.23)* 290 m (950 ft)/min
Absolute ceiling: 6,100 m (20,000 ft)
Range: *(standard S.23 and S.33)* 660–703 nm (1,245–1,300 km; 760–810 miles); *(S.30)* 1,129–1,624 nm (2,092–3,010 km; 1,300–1,870 miles); *(S.30 flight refuelled)* 2,171–2,952 nm (4,023–5,471 km; 2,500–3,400 miles)

Variants
S.23. Initial version of the C-class Empire flying-boat, as described under NOTES. Twenty-eight ordered for Imperial Airways and three for Qantas. Order included special long-range versions, named *Caledonia*, *Cambria* and *Cavalier*.
S.23/M. Two S.23s impressed into RAF service after the loss of S.30 types *Cabot* and *Caribou*. Each S.23/M, originally Imperial's *Cordelia* and *Clio*, carried ASV radar and Boulton-Paul four-gun dorsal and tail turrets. Could carry six depth charges internally. *Clio* lost after engine failure in August 1941 but *Cordelia* handed back to BOAC at end of the year.
S.30. Nine flying-boats, all used by Imperial Airways/BOAC (Airways [Atlantic] Ltd) except for two that went to TEAL. Four had flight refuelling capability. Strengthened structure and Perseus engines replacing Pegasus.
S.33. Final Empire flying-boats with Pegasus engines and short-range fuel tanks married to S.30 hull. Two completed.

Clifton in wartime colours

S.25 SUNDERLAND, S.25/V SANDRINGHAM and HYTHE CLASS

First flight: (Sunderland) 16 October 1937

Types: Four-engined military (Sunderland) and commercial flying-boats

Notes and Structure: The Sunderland was designed to fulfil the requirements of Air Ministry Specification R.2/33 for a four-engined long-range reconnaissance flying-boat, to replace earlier biplane types then in RAF service. Short Brothers used all its experience with the Empire flying-boat in the design of the larger Sunderland and the prototype flew the year after the Empire had begun its trials. Sunderland Is went into RAF service to replace Singapore IIIs in mid-1938, first to Squadron Nos 210 and 230. By the outbreak of the Second World War the RAF had three Sunderland squadrons. The Sunderland is remembered in the annals of the RAF as the first flying-boat to be equipped with power-operated gun turrets.

The Sunderland was a cantilever high-wing monoplane. The wing structure was all-metal; with the exception of the trailing-edge portion of the ailerons, the complete wings, including the Gouge flaps, were metal covered. The hull was a two-step structure, again all-metal, with a maximum depth of 5.41 m (17 ft 9 in). The cantilever tail unit was all-metal, except for the movable surfaces which were fabric covered aft of the leading edge, and

had inset trimming tabs. Defensive armament was eight 0.303-in machine guns installed in Fraser-Nash nose and tail turrets, although other guns were carried as detailed under ARMAMENT. Accommodation was divided into two decks. On the upper deck was the flight compartment forward for two pilots, a radio operator, a navigator and engineer. Aft of the spar frames were kept the reconnaissance flares and stowage for maintenance cradles. In the extreme nose was the bomb-aimer's position and nose turret. This turret could slide aft to permit easy mooring of the flying-boat. Aft of the turret on the lower deck was the mooring compartment, from which a ladder led to the upper deck. On the starboard side of the ladder was the toilet, while on the port side a gangway led to the officers' wardroom. Further aft was the galley, bomb compartment and crew quarters. In the rear end of the hull was the work bench, the inflatable dinghy, flares and sea-markers.

The Sunderland was produced in several military versions, the total number built being 721. The last, a Mk V, was completed by Blackburn Aircraft at Dumbarton on 19 October 1945. The flying-boat was a great wartime success, contributing valuable work on reconnaissance and patrol duties. It claimed its first German U-boat in January 1940 and was also employed as a transport. After the war Sunderlands continued to serve with the RAF until May 1959, the last operational mission being that carried out by the combined 205 and 209 Squadrons stationed at Seletar on the 15th. The

Sunderland GR.Mk Vs

Blackburn-built Sunderland V operated postwar by the French Navy

confined to secondary structural changes and to the complete rearrangement of the interior. Apart from the recontouring of the nose and tail to eliminate the characteristics of the military version, the mooring compartment in the bow was provided with equipment more closely following that of the Empire flying-boats. The passenger accommodation was arranged on two decks, the general furnishings and finish to the requirements of the various companies which ordered the aircraft. Details of these aircraft can be found under VARIANTS.

BOAC ended its Hythe class operations on 16 February 1949 but three aircraft and later a further seven were purchased by Mr Barry Aikman. Three of these took part in the Berlin airlift from August 1948 (which had started on 24 June, with USAF transports) and subsequently the flying-boats comprised the bulk of his Aguila Airways fleet that initially operated a Lisbon–Madeira service.

actual last flight was made on 24 May, by a single aircraft. By then the Sunderland had served the RAF for 21 years, the longest period of any aircraft up to that time, and its departure from service also marked the end of the RAF's use of water-based aircraft. However, Sunderlands supplied to the Royal New Zealand Air Force continued to serve operationally until 1966. The French Navy had also been a postwar operator.

During the postwar period Sunderlands had seen considerable action, perhaps the best remembered being that performed on 21 April 1949 when a single aircraft landed on the Yangtse River to carry a doctor and medical supplies to the British frigate HMS *Amethyst*, which had been fired upon and trapped by Chinese communist forces (before escaping). On 22 August 1950 the announcement was made that RAF Sunderlands were being used in the blockade of the west coast of Korea (following the start of the Korean War on 25 June, when North Korean forces crossed the 38th Parallel into South Korea), and Sunderlands were flown in Malaysia.

Returning to 1943, in that year Sunderlands were supplied to BOAC (British Overseas Airways Corporation) to augment its fleet of overseas transports and were known under the collective title of Hythe class. Gun turrets and all associated military equipment had been removed and the interior of each flying-boat refitted to meet airline requirements. Details of this class can be found under VARIANTS.

Further commercial flying-boats were produced from Sunderlands as Sandringhams, and these had properly recontoured noses and tails where the guns had previously been. The modifications were

Data
Accommodation: See VARIANTS
Power plants: See VARIANTS
Wing span: *(Sunderland, Hythe and Sandringham)* 34.37 m (112 ft 9½ in)
Wing area, gross: *(Sunderland, Hythe and Sandringham)* 156.73 m² (1,687 sq ft)
Length overall: *(Sunderland, Hythe and Sandringham)* 26.01 m (85 ft 4 in)
Height overall: *(Sunderland, Hythe and Sandringham)* 10.02 m (32 ft 10½ in)
Weight empty: *(Sunderland I)* 13,875 kg (30,589 lb); *(Sunderland II)* 14,968 kg (33,000 lb); *(Sunderland III)* 15,649 kg (34,500 lb); *(Sunderland V)* 16,783 kg (37,000 lb); *(Hythe)* 15,055 kg (33,190 lb); *(Sandringham 1 day version)* 15,490 kg (34,150 lb); *(Sandringham 2, 3, 4 and 6, equipped)* 18,765 kg (41,370 lb); *(Sandringham 5 and 7)* 17,917 kg (39,500 lb)
Max t/o weight: *(Sunderland I)* 22,226 kg (49,000 lb); *(Sunderland II and III)* 26,308 kg (58,000 lb); *(Sunderland V and Sandringham 5 and 7)* 27,215 kg (60,000 lb); *(Hythe)* 24,948 kg (55,000 lb); *(Sandringham 1, 2, 3, 4 and 6)* 25,400 kg (56,000 lb)
Max level speed: *(Sunderland I)* 181 knots 336 km/h; 209 mph); *(Sunderland II)* 178 knots (330 km/h; 205 mph); *(Sunderland III)* 182 knots (338 km/h; 210 mph); *(Sunderland V)* 185 knots (343 km/h; 213 mph); *(Hythe)* As for respective Sunderland; *(Sandringham 1)* 187 knots (346 km/h; 215 mph); *(Sandringham 2, 3, 4 and 6)* 205 knots (380 km/h; 236 mph); *(Sandringham 5 and 7)* 179 knots (331 km/h; 206 mph)

BOAC's Hythe class flying-boat *Hawksbury* GHZ

Rate of climb at s/l: *(Sunderland III)* 219 m (720 ft)/min; *(Sunderland V)* 256 m (840 ft)/min; *(Sandringham 1)* 170 m (557 ft)/min
Service ceiling: *(Sunderland I)* 4,572 m (15,000 ft); *(Sunderland III)* 4,875 m (16,000 ft); *(Sunderland V)* 5,455 m (17,900 ft); *(Sandringham 1)* 4,315 m (14,150 ft); *(Sandringham 2)* 5,700 m (18,700 ft)
Range: *(Sunderland I)* 2,171 nm (4,025 km; 2,500 miles); *(Sunderland V)* 2,588 nm (4,796 km; 2,980 miles); *(Sandringham 1)* 1,389–2,214 nm (2,575–4,104 km; 1,600–2,550 miles); *(Sandringham 2 with 32 passengers, 3, 4,*

Australis, one of three Sunderland IIIs operated between Sydney and Lord Howe Island by Trans-Oceanic Airways during 1947–1952, seen here at Laucala Bay in 1947 *(Rob Wight)*

and 6) 2,110 nm (3,911 km; 2,430 miles); *(Sandringham 5 and 7)* 2,128 nm (3,943 km; 2,450 miles)
Normal range: *(Sunderland III)* 1,546 nm (2,865 km; 1,780 miles)
Overload range: *(Sunderland III)* 2,518 nm (4,667 km; 2,900 miles)
Endurance: *(Sunderland III)* 13½ h; *(Sunderland V)* 15 h
Armament: *(Sunderland V)* Two 0.303-in machine guns in Fraser-Nash nose turret and four in Fraser-Nash tail turret. Two 0.5-in manually operated beam guns, plus four fixed Browning guns remotely controlled in the bow. Two-gun dorsal turret. Bombs, depth charges, mines, etc up to a weight of 907 kg (2,000 lb) carried on railed racks. Dorsal turret later removed.

The one and only Sandringham 1 as operated under trial conditions by BOAC and still carrying military serials

Variants
S.25 Sunderland I. Initial version for the RAF with 753 kW (1,010 hp) Bristol Pegasus XXII nine-cylinder air-cooled and medium-supercharged radial engines. Armament of 0.303-in machine guns, one (then two) in the Fraser-Nash nose turret and four in tail turret plus two Vickers beam guns. Crew of 7, then 10.
S.25 Sunderland II. Four 794 kW (1,065 hp) Pegasus XVIII engines with two-speed superchargers. Two-gun Fraser-Nash dorsal turret usually in place of the manually operated beam guns, plus nose and tail armament of later Mk Is. ASV Mk II search radar.
S.25 Sunderland III. Same engines as Mk II. Modified hull with streamlined front step. Dorsal turret standard. Later models also with fixed guns in nose and side hatch guns. Also supplied to RAAF.

S.25 Sunderland V. 895 kW (1,200 hp) Pratt & Whitney R-1830-90B fourteen-cylinder air-cooled radial engines driving three-blade Hamilton Standard Hydromatic full-feathering propellers.

Hythe class. At the end of 1942 six Sunderland IIIs in production for the RAF were stripped of military equipment and were operated (from March 1943) by BOAC as camouflaged civil flying-boats. The first of these was registered G-AGER and named *Hadfield* but the first to appear was G-AGJM *Hythe*, hence the class name. A seventh Sunderland III conversion became *Hamble* to replace a lost aircraft, followed by 17 more from Sunderland IIIs. In 1946 three further Sunderland IIIs became G-AHEO to R with BOAC, one for freight services, and then in the following year a

Sandringham 3 *Brazil*, **also destined for Argentina, delivered in January 1946**

Sandringham 5 *Portsmouth*, **one of BOAC's Plymouth class**

Sandringham 1. Single prototype conversion of a Sunderland III into a fully civil-contoured flying-boat for BOAC, with 745 kW (1,000 hp) Bristol Pegasus 38 engines and de Havilland three-blade constant-speed propellers. Accommodation for 24 passengers by day and 16 by night, with a crew of seven. Dining saloon and cocktail bar on upper deck. Underwent trials with BOAC but subsequently operated by Aguila Airways.

Sandringham 2. 895 kW (1,200 hp) Pratt & Whitney R-1830-92 Twin Wasp radial engines driving Hamilton Standard Hydromatic three-blade propellers. Accommodation for 45 by day (28 on

Sandringham 4 *VH-BRC* **had formerly been operated by Ansett with another Sandringham purchased from Qantas (originally a TEAL aircraft) and was still flying to Lord Howe Island in the 1960s. It was subsequently purchased by Antilles Air Boats of the Virgin Islands and was the last Sandringham in commercial service. This photograph was taken while it was moored at Pago-Pago in 1974** (Keith Sissons)

final Hythe-class conversion of a Sunderland V became G-AHJR. BOAC services with this class of flying-boat began with Poole–Lagos schedules, followed by a route to Karachi which was later progressively extended to Rangoon. Initial Hythe Type H.1 model accommodated 16 passengers by day or night, followed by Type H.2 with promenade deck and Type H.3 for 22 day passengers. Stowages for three extra dinghies.

Civil Sunderlands. Sunderlands converted for commercial use but not of BOAC's Hythe class or Sandringhams included a Sunderland V for Aguila Airways, two 45-passenger Sunderland IIIs for the Uruguayan airline CAUSA (which also received a Mk V), two Sunderland Vs for Aerolineas Argentinas, five ex-RNZAF Sunderlands for New Zealand National Airways and Ansett and three ex-RAAF Sunderlands to Trans-Oceanic Airways.

Sandringham 6 *Kvitbjørn*, one of the original three such aircraft for DNL.

Sandringham 7 *Saint George*, a BOAC Bermuda class flying-boat

lower deck and 17 on upper deck, with a crew of six). Cocktail bar on upper deck. Two delivered to Argentine airline at the end of 1945.

Sandringham 3. As for Mk 2 except fitted for 21 day passengers. Dining saloon and galley on upper deck. Sperry A3 autopilot. Two delivered to Argentine airline in 1946. According to 1951–52 *Jane's*, Sandringham 2s and 3s were operated by Aviacion del Litoral Fluvial Argentina.

Sandringham 4. 895 kW (1,200 hp) Pratt & Whitney R-1830-90D Twin Wasp engines. As for Mk 2 except fitted for 30 day passengers. Pantry on upper deck. Four supplied to Tasman Empire Airways (TEAL). Operated until the end of 1949

on a route between Sydney, Australia, and Auckland, New Zealand. Sold thereafter.

Sandringham 5. As for Mk 4 except fitted for 22 day passengers or 16 night passengers. Pantry on lower deck. Nine supplied to BOAC, as Plymouth class.

Sandringham 6. As for Mk 3 except fitted for 37 day passengers on single deck. Pantry at forward end. Five supplied to Norwegian Air Lines (DNL).

Sandringham 7. As for Mk 4 except accommodation for 30 passengers. Three delivered to BOAC and operated between 1947 and 1950. Known by BOAC as Bermuda class.

SHORT-MAYO COMPOSITE (S.20/S.21)

First flight: 20 January 1938

Type: Long-range commercial transport

Notes and Structure: In 1919 Alcock and Brown proved that the North Atlantic (west to east) could be flown non-stop by aeroplane, although their perilous flight ended in a crash landing in Ireland. Despite the tremendous improvements in airframes and engines by the early 1930s, it had not proved possible to establish a commercial aeroplane service between Britain and the United States of America. The east–west route across the Atlantic, against the prevailing winds, was the most challenging, and with passengers on board aeroplanes would be expected to carry more fuel

than needed for the actual crossing to allow safety margins in range.

It had long been appreciated that an aeroplane could sustain flight at much higher weight than at which it could take off, and experiments conducted in several countries (like those of the *Zveno* bomber/fighter type conducted in the Soviet Union) had also shown that aeroplanes could be air launched safely from larger aircraft. On another track, flight refuelling experiments had also shown that range could be greatly enhanced by refilling an aeroplane's tanks after it had burned fuel at take-off. But flight refuelling had its own problems and this was still very much experimental. Certainly commercial pilots also disliked the idea of flying so close to another aeroplane. Therefore, in 1935 The Mayo Composite Aircraft Company was established to acquire and handle the world rights in the Composite Aircraft invented and patented by Major R. H. Mayo. This concept was seen as an alternative to flight refuelling, not a replacement, and could only be applied to smaller long-range aircraft on non-passenger commercial operations.

The Composite Aircraft concept involved the use of a large aircraft to carry into the air a small heavily laden aeroplane, the smaller machine mounted on top of the larger and comparatively lightly loaded aircraft. The Composite was expected to take-off easily and quickly under ordinary operating conditions and then, at a suitable height, the upper component would be released from the lower in such a way that the two aircraft would separate rapidly in a vertical plane without the risk of fouling or collision. The key to the practicability of the invention was the means to ensure the safe separation. Once the upper component had separated, carrying fuel and a payload with which it would have been incapable of taking off by itself, the lower component was to return to base leaving the upper to make the long-distance journey and land in a conventional way. Both aircraft were to be capable of separate operation if required, carrying the appropriate payload and fuel for normal take off. The Composite concept was seen as appropriate to commercial and military applications.

The Composite concept appealed to the Air Ministry, which ordered a composite 'pair' from Short Brothers at Rochester for experimental use by Imperial Airways. This consisted of a large flying-boat and an upper component seaplane. The specification required the upper component to have a range of approximately 3,500 miles when carrying 1,000 lb of mail, sufficient for the direct North Atlantic crossing in a continuous headwind averaging 60 mph. Significantly, as take-off with a heavy load was not a problem, this specification could be met by a seaplane with only 1,480 hp available from its engines.

The S.21 lower component, built as S.797 (Short manufacture number) and civil registered G-ADHK, was virtually a standard Empire flying-boat but with an increase in wing span and carrying a support structure above the fuselage. This aircraft was later named *Maia* and flew for the first time by itself on 27 July 1937. The S.20 upper seaplane, built as S.796 and registered G-ADHJ, made its maiden flight on 5 September 1937 and was named *Mercury*. The seaplane was a cantilever high-wing monoplane powered by four Napier-Halford Rapier V, later VI, 16-cylinder engines. It was of all-metal construction, except for the fabric-covered ailerons, rudder and elevators, and accommodated a pilot and wireless operator plus mail or freight.

The first take-off in coupled composite configuration was achieved on 20 January 1938, followed by the first separation in flight on 6 February 1938. After satisfactorily completing the manufacturer's trials and passing through the

The Composite Aircraft, with *Mercury* attached to *Maia*

Mercury detaches itself from *Maia* while cruising over Foynes at the beginning of its journey to Montreal, 21 July 1938 *(Charles E. Brown)*

MAEE at Felixstowe, the Composite was handed over to Imperial Airways for experimental operation. On 21 July the Composite took off from Foynes, Eire, and after separation the *Mercury* seaplane flew non-stop to Montreal carrying the first commercial load across the North Atlantic by a heavier-than-air aircraft. Captain D. C. T. Bennett, in control of *Mercury*, landed the following day after a flying time of 20 h 20 min. The payload was the full 454 kg (1,000 lb) of newspapers and photographs. After refuelling, *Mercury* flew on to New York, completing the total distance from Foynes to New York in a flying time of 22 h 31 min. The return journey by *Mercury* was made in easy stages, flying from New York to Botwood (Newfoundland) on 25 July; from Botwood to Horta (Azores) the following day; and from Horta to Southampton by way of Lisbon on 27 July.

Having proved itself, it was decided the Composite should attempt a world distance record: between 6 and 8 October 1938 *Mercury* flew 5,211.66 nm (9,652 km; 5,997.5 miles) from Dundee, Scotland, to the Orange River, South Africa, carrying extra fuel in its sealed floats. This was the longest distance covered by any sea-going aircraft at that time and in 1984 remains a world record for seaplanes in Class C.2. The actual flying time was 42 h 5 min.

That Christmas *Mercury* was launched twice to carry mail to Alexandria, its ton of mail for each

flight accommodated in the fuselage compartment and floats. With such exceptional capability, Imperial Airways conceived the idea of using further Composites but based on the huge 40-passenger Armstrong Whitworth Ensign four-engined landplane airliner as the launch aircraft. However, this was denied the national airline. During the winter months and thereafter *Mercury* could not use icebound Botwood and so remained inactive, while *Maia* was used temporarily as a 10-passenger airliner (although it had possible accommodation for 24 passengers plus mail) between Southampton and Foynes to feed the Empire flying-boats on experimental transatlantic service. With the outbreak of war the Composite's commercial operations came to an untimely end. For a period during 1940–41 *Mercury* was operated as a training seaplane by No 320 Squadron, RAF, comprising Dutch aircrew that had escaped the German occupation, but was scrapped in 1941. *Maia* was destroyed in a bombing raid while at Poole Harbour on 11 May that year. With the exception of military pick-a-back aircraft like the German *Mistel* composites flown during the Second World War, and postwar experimental aircraft such as the French ramjet-powered Leduc series carried above launching airliners and the US Space Shuttle Orbiter while transported by Boeing 747, the composite concept died with the Short-Mayo.

Data

Accommodation: See NOTES

Power plant: *(Mercury)* Four Napier-Halford Rapier Mk V, then VI, engines; *(Maia)* Four 682 kW (915 hp) Bristol Pegasus X radial engines

Wing span: *(Mercury)* 22.25 m (73 ft); *(Maia)* 34.75 m (114 ft)

Wing area, gross: *(Mercury)* 56.76 m² (611 sq ft); *(Maia)* 162.58 m² (1,750 sq ft)

Length overall: *(Mercury)* 15.52 m (50 ft 11 in); *(Maia)* 25.88 m (84 ft 11 in)

Height overall: *(Mercury)* 6.17 m (20 ft 3 in); *(Maia)* 9.94 m (32 ft 7½ in)

Weight empty: *(Mercury)* 4,610 kg (10,163 lb); *(Maia as lower component)* 11,626 kg (25,631 lb); *(Maia as normal flying-boat)* 11,224 kg (24,745 lb)

Crew and payload: *(Mercury)* 608 kg (1,340 lb)

Max t/o weight: *(Mercury)* 9,435 kg (20,800 lb); *(Maia as lower component)* 12,700 kg (28,000 lb); *(Maia as normal flying-boat)* 17,236 kg (38,000 lb); *(Composite Aircraft)* 22,135 kg (48,800 lb)

Max level speed: *(Mercury)* 184 knots (341 km/h; 212 mph); *(Maia)* 174 knots (322 km/h; 200 mph)

Normal cruising speed: *(Mercury)* 158 knots (293 km/h; 182 mph); *(Composite Aircraft)* 126 knots (233 km/h; 145 mph)
Rate of climb at s/l: *(Mercury)* 305 m (1,000 ft)/min; *(Composite Aircraft)* 244 m (800 ft)/min
Service ceiling: *(Maia)* 6,100 m (20,000 ft)
Take-off time: *(Composite Aircraft)* 18 sec
Standard range at cruising speed: *(Mercury)* 3,387 nm (6,276 km; 3,900 miles)

Standard duration at cruising speed: *(Mercury)* 21½ h
Range: *(Maia)* 738 nm (1,368 km; 850 miles)

Variants
S.20 Mercury. Seaplane upper component for the Composite Aircraft. As described above.
S.21 Maia. Modified Empire-type flying-boat used as lower component of Composite Aircraft.
Short-Mayo Composite. Name of the combined *Maia/Mercury.*

BRISTOL BOMBAY and HANDLEY PAGE H.P.53 HEREFORD

First flight (Short built): (Bombay) March 1939
(Hereford) 17 May 1939

Types: Twin-engined bomber-transport (Bombay); twin-engined medium bomber and bomber crew trainer (Hereford)
Notes and Structure: To a 1931 specification for a bomber-transport for the RAF, Bristol developed its Type 130 Bombay, which first flew as a prototype on 23 June 1935. Gaining a production order along with its rival, the H.P.54 Harrow from Handley Page (the A.W.23 from Armstrong Whitworth failed to win an order), the Bristol Aeroplane Company found itself too busy on its Blenheim work to put the Bombay into production and so Short & Harland of Belfast was contracted to produce 80 under Specification 47/36. As men-

tioned in the Introduction, Short & Harland had been formed in mid-1936 as a result of an agreement between Short Brothers (Rochester and Bedford) and the shipbuilders Harland & Wolff, the latter company which had been responsible for the production of de Havilland D.H.6 and Avro 504s during the First World War, together with a very small number of Handley Page V/1500 heavy bombers.

The Bombay represented the first production by the new company at Belfast. However, of the 80 ordered, which represented the total number of Bombays contracted for, only 50 were delivered as L5808 to L5857. Of these, five were fitted with dual controls. The remainder of the contract, up to L5887, was cancelled to allow Shorts to concentrate its efforts on the Hereford. The reason for this was simple: the Bombay went into service from March 1939, by which time it was obsolete. Nevertheless it served with two transport squadrons and a night-bomber/transport squadron of the RAF during the Second World War, flying in the transport role in the Mediterranean and

Short & Harland-built Bristol Bombay bomber-transport

Line up of production Herefords in RAF camouflage

Middle East theatres of war and took on an offensive role in North Africa. As can be seen from the accompanying illustration, the Bombay was a cantilever high-wing monoplane with a non-retractable undercarriage. It was of all-metal construction and in production form was powered by two 753 kW (1,010 hp) Bristol Pegasus XXII radial engines. Defensive armament comprised Vickers machine guns in manually-operated nose and tail turrets and bombs could be stowed internally. As a troop carrier it could accommodate 24 persons or bulky freight could be carried.

In 1936 Handley Page flew the prototype of an unusually configured high-performance medium bomber known subsequently as the Hampden. Along with an initial production order for Hampdens, Specification B.44/36 was issued for the simultaneous production of a variant with Napier Dagger engines instead of Pegasus radials. The second Hampden prototype was so modified and in this form it made its maiden flight at the beginning of July 1937. Thereafter it was sent to Short & Harland's Queen's Island factory to assist in the Hereford production programme, to be undertaken by Short & Harland. Like the Hampden, the Hereford was a four-seater with rather restricted accommodation. It had an all-metal structure with stressed skin covering except for fabric over the flaps, ailerons, rudders and elevators. Six machine guns were carried for defence and the 1,814 kg (4,000 lb) bombload was stowed internally in the deep forward section of the 'panhandle' fuselage.

The first contract for 100 Herefords covered L6002 to L6101, and the Hereford went into service in 1940. However the 712 kW (955 hp) Dagger VIII inline engines proved troublesome, even though problems had not shown themselves during the Air Ministry's 100 hour Type Test. As a result, the 24-cylinder 'H' type Dagger engine quickly gave way to the Sabre 'I' type on Napier production lines. Of the Herefords, nine were later converted to Hampdens and the aircraft covered by the follow-on contract for 50 Herefords, N9055 to N9081 and N9084 to N9106, were mostly either converted to Hampdens or built as such, including one configured as a prototype Hampden torpedo bomber for Coastal Command.

Data
Power plant: See NOTES

Bombay
Wing span: 29.18 m (95 ft 9 in)
Wing area, gross: 124.49 m² (1,340 sq ft)
Length overall: 21.11 m (69 ft 3 in)
Height overall: 5.94 m (19 ft 6 in)
Weight empty: 6,260 kg (13,800 lb)
Max t/o weight: 9,072 kg (20,000 lb)
Max level speed: 167 knots (309 km/h; 192 mph) at 1,980 m (6,500 ft)
Service ceiling: 7,620 m (25,000 ft)
Range: 1,936 nm (3,590 km; 2,230 miles)

Hereford/Hampden I
Wing span: 21.08 m (69 ft 2 in)
Wing area, gross: 62.06 m² (668 sq ft)
Length overall: 16.33 m (53 ft 7 in)
Height overall: 4.55 m (14 ft 11 in)
Weight empty: 5,343 kg (11,780 lb)
Max t/o weight: 8,508 kg (18,756 lb)
Max permissible t/o weight: 9,525 kg (21,000 lb)
Max level speed: *(Hereford)* 230 knots (426 km/h; 265 mph); *(Hampden I)* 221 knots (409 km/h; 254 mph)
Service ceiling: 5,790 m (19,000 ft)
Range with full bombload: 1,042 nm (1,931 km; 1,200 miles)
Armament: See NOTES

Variants
Bristol Bombay. All production Bombays built by Short & Harland. Only 50 of 80 ordered were completed.
Handley Page Hereford. All production Herefords built by Short & Harland, initial contract totalling 100. Another 50 ordered were mostly either built as, or converted to, Hampden Is. After some operational use, Herefords were relegated to training bomber crews.

S.29 STIRLING and S.31 M-4

First flight: (Stirling) 14 May 1939

Types: Four-engined heavy bomber (Stirling); scale model bomber (M-4)

Notes and Structure: In 1936 the growing strength of the German Luftwaffe had alarmed the Air Ministry into issuing Specification B.12/36 covering a modern four-engined heavy bomber for the RAF. A second specification covered a twin-engined bomber. The requirements were not too difficult to fulfil, which included the provision for a crew of six, a cruising speed of at least 200 knots (370 km/h; 230 mph) and a cruising range of 1,300 nm (2,415 km; 1,500 miles) with the normal warload, a maximum range twice that of the cruising range and a maximum bombload of 6,350 kg (14,000 lb). Within the specification, however, the Ministry failed to fully appreciate the likely operational requirements of future years and to some extent the potential of the B.12/36 bomber was severely restricted by the call for a maximum wing span of 30.50 m (100 ft) to suit existing aircraft hangars, a bomb-bay capable of carrying bombs no greater than 4,000 lb in weight, and the capability of flying from the existing runways from which biplanes were then operating.

B.12/36 was seen by the British aircraft industry as potentially a most lucrative specification and submissions were sent in by Short Brothers, Supermarine, Armstrong Whitworth, Avro, Bristol, Handley Page, Hawker and Vickers. In the event the first two each received a contract to build two prototypes, producing the Short S.29 Stirling and the Supermarine Type 317 and Type 318. The Supermarine prototypes were subsequently bombed out of existence by the Luftwaffe and thus never flew.

For its time the Short design incorporated many novel and previously untried features and so it was decided that the layout should be flight tested first on a half-scale model, before a prototype was

completed. This model became the S.31 M-4, which flew for the first time on 19 September 1938. It was a near exact scale model of the S.29, powered initially by four Pobjoy Niagara III engines of 67 kW (90 hp) each and later by more powerful Niagara IVs.

The first prototype Stirling (L7600) was fitted with four Bristol Hercules II engines. This crashed on landing after its maiden flight but the second prototype was ready by August that year. These prototypes and early production aircraft, which were being delivered by August 1940 to become the RAF's first four-engined monoplane bombers and its first four-engined heavy bombers since the Handley Page V/1500 biplane of First World War design, were built by the parent company. However, although the majority of the 2,381 Stirlings completed during the Second World War emerged from Shorts, a dispersal organisation was put into operation soon after production got underway whereby the main components were built in more than twenty different factories, in addition to a large sub-contracting scheme for the supply of small components.

The RAF's first operational Stirling squadron

A Stirling I emerges from the factory, with another minus its engines to the rear

The half-scale Stirling, the M-4, at Rochester Airport

was No 7. This squadron carried out the first RAF four-engined heavy bomber attack of the war, when three aircraft led by Sqn Ldr Griffith-Jones struck at Rotterdam on the night of 10/11 February 1941. During the course of the war Stirlings carried out more than 18,400 missions, but the appearance of the Handley Page Halifax in RAF service from the end of 1940, and some time later the Avro Lancaster, quickly degraded the Stirling's importance as an offensive aircraft. Versions of the Stirling built after 1943 took on new roles, important to the overall war effort but less glamorous.

The Stirling was a cantilever mid-wing monoplane, using a two-spar all-metal wing structure similar to that of the Empire flying-boat. Gouge type trailing-edge flaps were adopted, with a chord equal to 48 per cent of the total wing chord. The rectangular-section (with rounded corners) fuselage was an all-metal structure built up of transverse frames covered with aluminium-alloy sheet with intercostal stiffeners. A normal crew comprised seven, made up of two pilots, navigator/bomb-aimer, front gunner/wireless operator, two air gunners, and a flight engineer/air gunner. Armament is detailed under VARIANTS.

Data
Power plant: *(Stirling I)* Four 1,189 kW (1,595 hp) Bristol Hercules XI fourteen-cylinder sleeve-valve radial engines; *(Stirling II)* four 1,193 kW (1,600 hp) Wright R-2600-A5B Cyclone fourteen-cylinder air-cooled radial engines; *(Stirling III)* four 1,230 kW (1,650 hp) Bristol Hercules VI or XVI fourteen-cylinder air-cooled radial engines; *(Stirling IV and V)* four

Cyclone-engined Stirling II

Destination Germany: loading nearly eight tons of bombs into a Stirling bomber *(Charles E. Brown)*

Bristol Hercules engines; *(S.31 M-4)* See NOTES
Wing span: *(Stirling)* 30.20 m (99 ft 1 in); *(S.31)* 15.11 m (49 ft 7 in)
Wing area, gross: *(Stirling)* 135.64 m² (1,460 sq ft); *(S.31)* 30.19 m² (325 sq ft)
Length overall: *(Stirling)* 26.59 m (87 ft 3 in); *(Stirling V only)* 27.60 m (90 ft 6¾ in); *(S.31)* 13.28 m (43 ft 7 in)
Height overall: *(Stirling)* 6.93 m (22 ft 9 in)
Weight empty: *(Stirling I and II)* 19,958 kg (44,000 lb); *(Stirling III)* 21,273 kg (46,900 lb)
Max t/o weight: *(Stirling I and II)* 26,943 kg (59,400 lb); *(Stirling III, IV and V)* 31,751 kg (70,000 lb); *(S.31)* 2,585 kg (5,700 lb)
Max level speed: *(Stirling I and II)* 226 knots (418 km/h; 260 mph); *(Stirling III)* 239 knots (443 km/h; 275 mph); *(Stirling IV and V)* 243 knots (451 km/h; 280 mph); *(S.31)* 160 knots (296 km/h; 184 mph)
Max rate of climb at s/l: *(Stirling III)* 244 m (800 ft)/min
Service ceiling: *(Stirling I and II)* 6,250 m (20,500 ft); *(Stirling IV and V)* 5,485 m (18,000 ft)
Range: *(Stirling I)* 2,023 nm (3,750 km; 2,330 miles); *(Stirling III)* 1,745 nm (3,235 km; 2,010 miles); *(Stirling IV and V)* 2,605 nm (4,828 km; 3,000 miles)
Armament: See VARIANTS

Variants
S.29 Stirling I. Initial production version with Hercules XI engines. Initial defensive armament of 0.303-in Browning machine guns in nose turret (2 guns), tail turret (4) and retractable ventral turret (2). Later, addition of dorsal turret and two side guns. 6,350 kg (14,000 lb) of bombs. Second most-produced version.

S.29 Stirling II. A version of the Mk I with US Cyclone engines, to be built in Canada. Two prototypes only.

S.29 Stirling III. Major production version with Hercules VI or, more commonly, XVI engines. Final bomber variant with dorsal turret and carrying an 8,165 kg (18,000 lb) bomb load.

S.29 Stirling IV. From the outset, the Stirling had been designed to be capable of fulfilling a secondary 24-troop transport role. Mk IV was a long-range troop transport version of the Mk III, with the nose and mid-upper turrets removed and replaced by fairings but with the four-gun tail turret retained. A large opening was introduced in the underside of the rear fuselage for dropping paratroopers. Bomb cells were retained and used for the carriage and dropping of airborne supplies. Crew of six. Aft of the rear spar, provision was made for accommodating 24 paratroopers or 34 airborne troops with weapons and equipment. Also capable of glider towing. Delivered from October 1943. Could tow two Horsa, five Hotspur or one large Hamilcar gliders. Stirling IVs towing

Stirling V transport with its nose door lifted

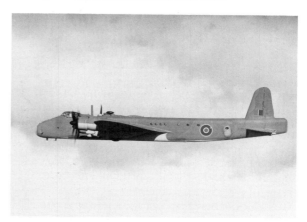

Stirling V transport

A jeep is loaded onto a Stirling V through the large side cargo door

Stirling III flying over Lough Neagh in early 1943

The 1,000th Stirling built by Short & Harland at Belfast was this Mk IV

Horsas were used on D-Day (6 June 1944) and on other famous actions of the war, including the crossing of the Rhine in 1945.

S.29 Stirling V. Unarmed military transport and freighter version of Mk III, which it resembled in general outline except for its redesigned nose. The forward portion of the nose was hinged upwards for loading light freight into the forward compartment, a self-contained beam block and tackle being provided for this purpose. Aft of the rear spar frame the fuselage could be adapted to suit a variety of duties, including that of military passenger transport for 14; ambulance for twelve

S.37 Silver Stirling photographed at Sydenham in May 1945

Main passenger cabin of the Silver Stirling

stretchers and sitting casualties; troop transport for 40 fully-armed men; paratroop transport for 20, with containers; or for heavy freighting to carry one jeep, trailer and 6-pdr gun complete with ammunition and crew of four, two jeeps and eight crew, 14 standard freight baskets or other loads. Large door in rear fuselage complete with portable loading ramps. Normal flight crew of five. Mk V went into RAF service from early 1945. Lowest-produced full production version, amounting to 160 examples. This version ended Stirling production in November 1945.

S.37 Stirling/civil conversion. The Short model number S.37 applied to a single military Stirling Mk V fitted out to civil airliner standard with 30 passenger seats. Also known as the Silver Stirling and flown in May 1945. Only commercially operated Stirlings were twelve Mk Vs flown by the Belgian airline Trans-Air, furnished by Airtech in equal numbers of 36-passenger airliners and freighters.

S.31. Known as M-4, single example of a half-scale model of Stirling bomber to flight test configuration. Pobjoy engines. Described under NOTES.

S.26 G-CLASS FLYING-BOAT

First flight: 21 July 1939

Type: Four-engined commercial flying-boat
Notes and Structure: The G-class flying-boat was a larger development of the Empire type for service over the North Atlantic. Three were ordered as *Golden Hind*, *Grenadier* and *Grenville*, the first of which was launched in June 1939. All three were delivered with blanked-off windows (*Grenadier* and *Grenville* having been renamed *Golden Hind* and *Golden Horn*), as it had been decided that until experience had been gained in the operation of a regular service across the North Atlantic only mail would be carried. However, it was always intended that passengers would eventually be carried by these aircraft.

Construction of the G-class was similar to that of the earlier C-class Empire, except that the hull had a Sunderland-type knife-edge rear step. As designed, the hull was divided into two decks. On the lower deck there was, in the extreme nose, the

Original configuration for the tail gun on *Golden Fleece*. Turbulence with this layout led to the adoption of a tail fairing from the fin, which meant the lower portion of the rudder had to be cut away

126

Golden Hind about to make its maiden flight in July 1939

mooring compartment, followed by two gentlemen's toilets. Next was to have been a pantry for serving meals in flight, a cocktail bar and lounge. Further aft, as planned, would be the four passenger cabins accommodating 24 day passengers or 20 night passengers, luxuriously furnished. The ladies' toilet compartment and baggage stowage was to occupy the remainder of the lower deck. The crew's compartment occupied all the upper deck forward of the front spar frame. Designed to give maximum comfort to the crew during long flights, there were the side-by-side seats for the two pilots (with dual controls), followed by the captain's seat and table, the radio operator's control station, the engineer's panel on the port side, and, by the navigator's chart table on the starboard side, a settee for the crew when resting. The remainder of the upper deck was occupied with mail compartments and stowage.

At the end of September 1939, soon after Imperial Airways had taken charge of *Golden Hind*, all three flying-boats were impressed into RAF service along with their crews. In fact only this single aircraft had flown by then. *Golden Horn* flew under civil registration in early 1940 before receiving its military modifications and serial number; *Golden Fleece* only flew in military markings.

For convoy escort and other expected military duties, all three G-class aircraft were camouflaged. They were fitted with Boulton-Paul four-gun turrets (two dorsal and one in the tail aft of the fin and rudder), radar, and equipped to carry eight 500 lb bombs under the wings and reconnaissance flares and other equipment within the hull. In this form they equipped the new No 119 Squadron, RAF, and for a few days carried military freight to the Middle East and Gibraltar. However, *Golden Fleece* had been lost with most of its crew on 20 June after experiencing engine trouble, and soon after the remaining aircraft were returned to Bri-

tain for repair. While they remained in RAF hands for the remainder of the year, *Golden Horn* and *Golden Hind* reverted to civil status in 1942 as 40-passenger transports flying out of Poole and bound in stages for Africa. *Golden Horn* was lost in early 1943 at Lisbon. After further flying between Poole and Ireland, and then services over the Indian Ocean as an airline-standard 38-passenger flying-boat, *Golden Hind* was refitted for postwar operation between England and Cairo carrying 24 passengers. These flights ended in September 1947, when BOACs final G-class flying-boat was sold.

Data
Accommodation: See NOTES
Power plant: Four 1,029 kW (1,380 hp) Bristol Hercules IV fourteen-cylinder double-row radial sleeve-valve engines.
Wing span: 40.94 m (134 ft 4 in)
Wing area: 200.67 m² (2,160 sq ft)
Length overall: 30.89 m (101 ft 4 in)
Height overall: 11.46 m (37 ft 7 in)
Weight empty: 17,102 kg (37,705 lb)
Payload and crew: 2,381 kg (5,250 lb)
Max t/o weight: 33,793 kg (74,500 lb)
Max level speed: 181 knots (336 km/h; 209 mph)
Cruising range: 2,779 nm (5,150 km; 3,200 miles)
Armament: See NOTES

Variants
S.26 G-class. As described under NOTES. Three only. No prewar commercial service. Two used by BOAC after military duty. Class known as *Golden Hind.*
S.26/M G-class. All three G-class flying-boats initially used for wartime military duties as long-range transports. Fully armed for convoy escort and anti-shipping roles. One lost. Two returned to civil use after No 119 Squadron was deactivated.

S.45 SEAFORD and S.45A SOLENT

First flight: (Sunderland IV/Seaford prototype) 30 August 1944

Types: Four-engined long-range reconnaissance and patrol flying-boat (Seaford); four-engined commercial flying-boat (Solent)

Notes and Structure: The Seaford was a development of the Sunderland flying-boat and was originally to have been the Sunderland IV. As considerable redesign was necessary to conform to the official Specification R.8/42, which called for an all-up weight of 34,019 kg (75,000 lb), more powerful engines and heavier armament, it was subsequently decided that the aircraft was no longer a Sunderland type but an aircraft of a new series; as such it was given the new type number S.45 and name Seaford.

Compared to the Sunderland, the hull of the Seaford had a bigger planing bottom with a 0.305 m (1 ft) increase in beam, a 1 m (3 ft 3 in) increase in length forward of the main step and a corresponding increase in the length aft. The wings were strengthened and the new tail unit had a dihedral tailplane and larger fin and rudder, the fin extending forward in a curve to the fuselage. The original Sunderland IV power plant was to consist of four 1,268 kW (1,700 hp) Bristol Hercules 19 engines but these were superseded by Hercules 100s. The new heavy armament comprised two 0.50-in machine guns in a Blockhouse power turret and fixed 0.303-in guns in the nose of the hull; two 20 mm cannon in a Bristol B-17 mid-upper turret and two 0.50-in beam guns; and two 0.50-in guns in a Glenn Martin tail turret. Bomb and depth-charge load was the same as that for the Sunderland V.

Two Seaford prototypes were ordered as MZ269 and MZ271 for armament and hydrodynamic research, plus a batch of production aircraft. The two prototypes were used for trials from April 1947 but both were lost in a fire. Meanwhile production of the Seaford proper had begun but, as improvements in performance over the latest version of the Sunderland were so limited, only eight were completed for evaluation by No 201 Squadron. After being rejected for the intended role, one was tested by Transport Command in unarmed transport form but was again unwanted. The first two production Seafords finished their careers at Felixstowe.

First Seaford prototype MZ269

128

BOAC Solent 2 *Somerset* dwarfs the hull of an old Sea Eagle formerly operated by Imperial Airways

Before the second production Seaford went to Felixstowe from Transport Command, it spent a brief time (during the winter if 1945–46) with BOAC for evaluation as a possible progenitor of commercial flying-boats of similar type. At last the Seaford had found its niche. Twelve new production S.45A Solent civil versions of the Seaford were ordered for BOAC with Hercules 637 engines of 1,260 kW (1,690 hp). The last of these, G-AHIY *Southsea*, was the final aircraft of any type to be constructed at Shorts' Rochester plant, launched on 8 April 1948.

The hull of each Solent was divided into two decks. On the upper deck were the crew compartment, galley and two passenger cabins; three passenger cabins, dressing rooms, a cocktail bar, toilets and a promenade cabin were on the lower deck. Each of the passenger cabins could be converted quickly to house bunk beds for night flying. The accommodation of each version of the Solent varied, and details of individual aircraft can be found under VARIANTS. The new Solents described above were known as Mk 2s and the only other new-production version was the Solent 4 for TEAL.

Data

Accommodation: See VARIANTS
Power plant: See NOTES and VARIANTS
Wing span: *(Seaford and Solent)* 34.37 m (112 ft 9½ in)
Wing area, gross: *(Solent and Seaford)* 156.73 m² (1,687 sq ft)
Length overall: *(Seaford and Solent)* 27.00 m (88 ft 6¾ in)
Height overall: *(Seaford and Solent)* 10.44 m (34 ft 3¼ in)
Weight empty: *(Seaford)* 20,411 kg (45,000 lb); *(Solent 2)* 21,664 kg (47,760 lb); *(Solent 3)* 21,868 kg (48,210 lb); *(Solent 4)* 22,294 kg (49,150 lb)
Typical service load: *(Seaford, incl crew)* 3,720 kg (8,200 lb)

Payload for max range: *(Solent 3)* 3,620 kg (7,980 lb); *(Solent 4)* 3,352 kg (7,390 lb)
Max t/o weight: *(Seaford, normal)* 34,019 kg (75,000 lb); *(Solent 2)* 35,380 lb (78,000 lb); *(Solent 3)* 35,652 kg (78,600 lb); *(Solent 4)* 36,287 kg (80,000 lb)
Max level speed: *(Seaford)* 210 knots (389 km/h; 242 mph); *(Solent 2)* 237 knots (439 km/h; 273 mph); *(Solent 3)* 232 knots (430 km/h; 267 mph); *(Solent 4)* 240 knots (444 km/h; 276 mph)
Rate of climb at s/l: *(Seaford)* 267 m (875 ft)/min; *(Solent 3)* 253 m (830 ft)/min; *(Solent 4)* 302 m (990 ft)/min; *(Solent 3 on three engines)* 101 m (330ft)/min
Service ceiling: *(Seaford)* 3,960 m (13,000 ft); *(Solent 3)* 4,725 m (15,500 ft); *(Solent 4)* 5,640 m (18,500 ft)
Range: *(Seaford, normal)* 2,432 nm (4,506 km; 2,800 miles); *(Seaford, overload range)* 2,692 nm (4,989 km; 3,100 miles); *(Solent 2)* 1,563 nm (2,897 km; 1,800 miles); *(Solent 3)* 1,910 nm (3,540 km; 2,200 miles) with 32 passengers at 165 knots (306 km/h; 190 mph); *(Solent 4)* 2,518 nm (4,667 km; 2,900 miles) with 27 passengers, baggage and 467 kg (1,030 lb) of freight, 3,051 Imperial gallons of fuel, at 174 knots (321 km/h; 200 mph)

Variants

S.45 Seaford. Two prototypes and eight production aircraft. Not used operationally. Six production Seafords converted to Solents.
Solent. Second production Seaford evaluated by BOAC as commercial flying-boat, temporarily with registration G-AGWU. Re-registered G-ANAJ and was named *City of Funchal* in service with Aguila Airways from 1954. (Aguila also acquired Solent 4s, previously owned by TEAL and then others.)

BOAC Solent 3 moored on the Thames in London

S.45A Solent 1. Original proposal for a commercial derivative of the Seaford, designed to carry 30 passengers by day and 24 by night. None built to this specification.

S.45A Solent 2. Twelve new production aircraft for BOAC with Hercules 637 engines and accommodation for 34 day passengers. Crew of seven.

Solent 3. Six ex-No 201 Squadron Seafords converted into 39-passenger Solent 3s for BOAC service. BOAC Solents first operated services from Southampton to Karachi.

Solent 4. Heaviest version of Solent for Tasman Empire Airways (TEAL). Four built as new, each with four Hercules 733 engines. Accommodation for 42 day passengers. Operated by original owner from mid-November 1949, to supersede Sandringhams on the airline's Auckland–Sydney route.

The first Solent 4 for TEAL, named *Aotearoa II*, which had been launched by Princess Elizabeth in May 1949

S.35 SHETLAND I and S.40 SHETLAND II

First flight: (Shetland I) 14 December 1944

Type: Long-range reconnaissance flying-boat; later prototype commercial flying-boat

Notes and Structure: Short Brothers in the period from the end of the First World War to the end of the Second World War is best remembered for its successful flying-boats, with perhaps the single exception of the Stirling bomber. However, while the best of these – the Empire and Sunderland – were large, the company had several notable failures (in commercial terms only) when it attempted to produce really outsized aircraft. The first gargantuan was, of course, the Cromarty, followed by the Sarafand and the Shetland, all of which were of sound design and performance but which failed to attract repeat orders.

The Shetland, the largest of all Short flying-boats, came about after considerable study by the Air Staff, Short and Saunders-Roe into a follow-on aircraft to the RAF's Sunderland. Eventually Specification R.14/40 was arrived at, which outlined a huge very-long-range flying-boat capable of reconnaissance and patrol while carrying anti-submarine and anti-shipping weapons. It was also clear that the design lent itself admirably to conversion into a commercial aircraft.

The Shetland was designed and constructed by Short Brothers with the collaboration of Saunders-Roe. The original layout was Shorts, which was responsible for the manufacture, assembly and flight testing of the aircraft; Saunders-Roe was responsible for the detail design and manufacture of component parts for the wings, including flaps, ailerons, engine mountings and wingtip floats. In general appearance the Shetland bore a striking resemblance to the earlier Imperial C-class and G-class flying-boats. With the exception of the fabric-covered Frise-type ailerons and tail control surfaces, it was entirely of metal construction.

Design of the Shetland had begun in 1940 and two prototypes were ordered. These were allocated type number S.35 by Shorts. However,

Having been reassigned as a military transport prototype, the Shetland I was painted silver

G-AGVD Shetland II civil flying-boat lifts-off from the Medway

before completion of the first prototype its role was changed to that of unarmed transport for the RAF. In this form the first Shetland prototype flew on 14 December 1944. The last minute change of role meant that a number of military features no longer required had already been incorporated into this prototype, not least of which were gun positions which had to be faired over with metal sheet. However, with the end of the war clearly in sight, the role of the Shetland was again revised, this time to that of commercial passenger flying-boat for BOAC. Unfortunately the existing prototype, which had continued flying postwar in military markings, was accidentally destroyed by fire while moored at Felixstowe.

The second prototype, also under construction during the war, was therefore completed as a commercial aircraft. This was civil registered and identified as a new model by the adoption of the Short number S.40 and name Shetland II. Launched at Rochester on 15 September 1947, it flew for the first time two days later. Apart from its obvious civil registration, the Shetland II was easily identifiable by its rounded nose (without gun turret fairing) and pointed tailcone. Accommodation was arranged, as requested, on two decks for a maximum of 40 passengers, yet the interior was fully capable of being configured for up to 70 passengers in a high standard of comfort. The flight compartment on the upper floor accommodated the pilot and co-pilot, a navigator, radio operator and engineer. On one side of this compartment was a stairway to the lower deck, behind which was

a settee that could be used also as two bunks for off-duty crew. From the flight compartment on the upper deck was the auxiliary engine room, then the main mail compartment, a kitchen, dining saloon/lounge for 12 persons, and a cocktail bar. From the latter was a staircase to the rear entry vestibule on the lower deck, with the Purser's office below the stairway. Opposite the stairway was a coat room and a men's dressing room. Baggage was stowed in the extreme tail. Above the dressing room was another mail or freight compartment. Forward of the vestibule on the lower deck were four cabins for passengers, each seating two. These doubled as two-berth cabins for night flights. Further along were four toilets, eight cabins for four day passengers or two by night and the forward entrance vestibule, at the sides of which were a ladies' toilet and dressing room.

The original Shetland had been powered by four 1,864 kW (2,500 hp) Bristol Centaurus VII radial engines; the Shetland II used similar Centaurus 660s, each driving a D.H. Hydromatic four-blade constant-speed full-feathering propeller. The total fuel capacity was a generous 27,785 litres (6,112 Imp gal). Despite all the work to suit the Shetland for civil operation, the era of the flying-boat had just about passed (at least for BOAC) and neither this aircraft, nor any possible production examples, were wanted for commercial operation. The Shetland II became an engine testbed, a bogus role that it performed until 1951, when it was broken up. Interestingly, Saunders-Roe also went ahead with a huge flying-boat of its own for BOAC, producing the ten-engined 105–220-seat Princess. This flew in 1952 but also remained a prototype.

131

Data

Accommodation: See NOTES
Power plant: See NOTES
Wing span: 45.82 m (150 ft 4 in)
Wing area, gross: 222.97 m² (2,400 sq ft)
Length overall: *(Shetland I)* 33.53 m (110 ft); *(Shetland II)* 32.92 m (108 ft)
Height overall: *(on beaching chassis)* 11.79 m (38 ft 8 in)
Weight empty: 34,420 kg (75,885 lb)
Max t/o weight: *(Shetland I)* 56,699 kg (125,000 lb); *(Shetland II)* 58,967 kg (130,000 lb)
Max level speed: 232 knots (430 km/h; 267 mph)
Max rate of climb at s/l with full load: 201 m (660 ft)-min
Range: *(Shetland I)* 4,038 nm (7,483 km; 4,650 miles) with 3,456 kg (7,620 lb) payload at 160 knots (296 km/h; 184 mph); *(Shetland I)* 2,605 nm (4,828 km; 3,000 miles) with 9,979 kg (22,000 lb) payload at 161 knots (298 km/h; 185 mph); *(Shetland I)* 1,803 nm (3,341 km; 2,076 miles) with 13,619 kg (30,025 lb) payload at 163 knots (303 km/h; 188 mph; *(Shetland II)* 2,605 nm (4,828 km; 3,000 miles) typically

Armament: As originally planned, electrically operated gun turrets in nose, dorsal and tail positions, each with two 0.50-in Browning machine guns. Heavy load of bombs, depth charges or mines.

Variants

S.35 Shetland I. Single prototype, described above. Planned as Sunderland replacement but revised to military transport and then civil transport roles. Destroyed by fire.
S.40 Shetland II. Second prototype, completed as commercial flying-boat and registered G-AGVD.

S.38/S.A.1 and S.39/S.A.2/S.B.9 STURGEON and S.B.3

First flight: (S.A.1) 7 June 1946

Types: Naval reconnaissance bomber (S.38); target-towing aircraft (S.39); and anti-submarine aircraft (S.B.3)

Notes and Structure: The Sturgeon was conceived during the Second World War as a twin-engined naval reconnaissance torpedo-bomber, intended for operation from the new HMS *Ark Royal* and *Hermes* class aircraft carriers. Two versions were projected by Shorts, one to be powered by the Bristol Centaurus radial engine and the other by two Rolls-Royce Merlin engines driving contra-rotating propellers. Subsequently Merlin-engined prototypes were built to revised Specification S.11/43.

The first two prototypes were Sturgeon FR.Mk 1s, intended as naval reconnaissance bombers with provision for two 0.50-in machine guns in the nose, eight rocket projectiles under each wing and one 1,000 lb or two 500 lb bombs or four depth charges in the internal fuselage bay.

By the time the prototype flew, the war with Japan had been won and the FAA no longer required such aircraft. Because of this, new Specification Q.1/46 was drawn up to convert the Sturgeon into a high-performance carrier-based target towing aircraft. The duties laid down for this aircraft were target towing for ground-to-air firing practice, photographic marking of ground-to-air firing, target towing for air-to-air firing practice by night and by day, 'throw-off' target practice, and radar calibration. These new requirements meant a redesign of the fuselage to provide two new camera positions, one in an extended nose and one in a dorsal position aft of the wings, and a re-arrangement of the interior to allow for a towing winch, target stowage, and new crew positions (two crew instead of the original pilot, navigator and radio operator). To keep the overall length within the required maximum of 13.72 m (45 ft) governed by the dimensions of the standard air-

RK787, the first prototype Sturgeon FR.Mk 1

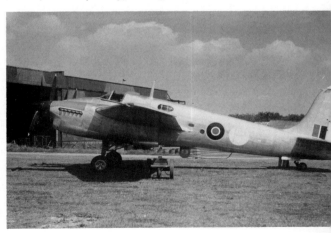

Sturgeon TT.Mk 2 in 1950

The first Sturgeon TT.Mk 2 with its nose down and wings
folded (Ministry of Defence)

craft carrier lift, the 1.52 m (5 ft) nose extension
was arranged to fold down.

Two new prototypes were built of the target-
towing Sturgeon and the first of these flew in 1948.
Twenty-three full production Sturgeon TT.Mk 2s
with 1,238 kW (1,660 hp) Merlin 140S engines
were delivered to the FAA as unarmed aircraft
(the first twin-engined aircraft designed for the
Navy from scratch to enter service), and these gave
valuable service along with the first prototype.
Meanwhile, on 12 August 1950 the last Sturgeon
of 24 originally ordered (23 delivered) became the
first prototype of an anti-submarine search aircraft
known to Shorts as S.B.3. This was the first Short
aeroplane to fly with turboprop engines – two
Armstrong Siddeley Mambas – but was not
selected for production against a version of the
Fairey Gannet. The second S.B.3 prototype was
not flown.

After fairly brief service on board ship, the

Sturgeon TT.Mk 2s were put ashore for good. At
the end of 1953 it was decided to convert these into
land-based target towing aircraft with carrier deck
equipment and the nose camera removed. The
resulting aircraft became Sturgeon TT.Mk 3s and
could be identified most easily by their shortened
fuselage noses. Although more were originally
planned, only five TT.Mk 2s became TT.Mk 3s
and these served on Malta until replaced by
Meteor TT.Mk 20 jets.

The Sturgeon TT.Mk 2 itself was a cantilever
mid-wing monoplane, with detachable wingtips
and hydraulically actuated folding outer wing sections. Of all-metal construction, the monocoque
fuselage structure was in four main sections consisting of a downward-folding nose, forward fuselage to the rear spar, rear fuselage to the leading-
edge of the fin, and the tail-end. Accommodation
was provided for a pilot and a navigator/winch
operator, the latter aft of the wings. The nose
camera position had optically flat panels in front
and on the starboard side for photographing
'throw-off' gunfire. Equipment carried by the aircraft included a Miles hydraulic target winch in the
lower fuselage, a dorsal camera for target marking
and three dinghies.

Data
Power plant: See NOTES
Wing span: (Sturgeon TT.Mk 2 and 3) 18.21 m
(59 ft 9 in); (S.B.3) 18.26 m (59 ft 11 in)
Wing area, gross: (TT.Mk 2 and 3) 52.07 m²
(560.4 sq ft)
Wing area, net: (S.B.3) 48.37 m² (520.6 sq ft)
Length overall: (TT.Mk 2) 14.91 m (48 ft 11 in);
(TT.Mk 3) 13.94 m (45 ft 9 in); (S.B.3) 13.64 m
(44 ft 9 in)

The second production Sturgeon TT.Mk 2 landing on
board ship

Height overall: *(TT.Mk 2)* 4.03 m (13 ft 2½ in)
Weight empty: *(TT.Mk 2)* 8,005 kg (17,647 lb);
(TT.Mk 3) 7,257 kg (16,000 lb); *(S.B.3)*
6,919 kg (15,252 lb)
Max t/o weight: *(TT.Mk 2)* 10,138 kg
(22,350 lb); *(TT.Mk 3)* 10,002 kg (22,050 lb);
(S.B.3) 10,705 kg (23,600 lb)
Max level speed: *(TT.Mk 2 and 3)* 318 knots
(589 km/h; 366 mph) at 7,375 m (24,200 ft);
(S.B.3) 278 knots (515 km/h; 320 mph)
Speed towing a 4.88 m (16 ft) winged target:
(TT.Mk 2) 251 knots (465 km/h; 289 mph)
Max rate of climb at s/l: *(TT.Mk 2)* 695 m
(2,280 ft)/min
Service ceiling: *(TT.Mk 2)* 10,700 m (35,200 ft)
**Endurance incl one hour towing a 9.76 m (32 ft)
winged target at 260 knots (483 km/h; 300 mph) at
4,575 m (15,000 ft):** 3¼ h
Range: *(S.B.3)* 621 nm (1,150 km; 715 miles)

Variants

S.A.1 Sturgeon FR.Mk 1. Two prototypes of a
naval reconnaissance bomber. Short type number
S.38.
S.A.2 Sturgeon TT.Mk 2. Production target towing aircraft for FAA. Short type number S.39.
Twenty-three full production examples.
S.B.9 Sturgeon TT.Mk 3. Designation of five
TT.Mk 2s with naval equipment deleted, for land
use.
S.B.3. Prototype anti-submarine search aeroplane
with a much-modified fuselage, Armstrong Siddeley Mamba turboprop engines, and carrying
underfuselage search radar.

**TS475, the first production TT.Mk 2 after conversion into
a land-based TT.Mk 3**

S.B.3 anti-submarine search prototype

NIMBUS

First flight: 18 January 1947

Type: Tandem two-seat glider
Notes and Structure: The Nimbus was a low-
mounted gull-wing sailplane intended for instruction and aerobatics. It had a wooden monocoque
fuselage of oval section, comprising spruce frames
covered with plywood. The wings were also of
wooden construction, except for fabric that
covered the area from the spars to the trailing
edges. The wings had constant taper in chord and
thickness, with the centre-section set at an acute
dihedral angle to the fuselage. The fabric covered
ailerons had variable droop. The tail unit was a
cantilever monoplane structure, with the small
dorsal and ventral fins constructed as an integral
part of the fuselage and the tailplane forward of
this on the upper fuselage. The elevators and
horn-balanced rudder were fabric covered. Spoil-
ers were incorporated into the upper wing surfaces. A conventional single wheel and tailskid
landing gear was fitted, the wheel partially streamlined by an underfuselage but integral skid that ran
from the nose.

Although the Nimbus was not begun as an official Short Brothers' project, its design was undertaken by members of the design staff at Rochester
and final construction was assisted by company
employees, resulting in the construction number
S.1312 being assigned to it. After completion the
Nimbus proved itself worthy of its origin and Short
Brothers was prepared to construct further
examples if orders followed from the British Gliding Association and others. However, this was not

to be. After the company moved to Belfast, the Nimbus was used to form a new company gliding club to take over from the previous club set up at Rochester. The Nimbus took part in competition and continued in use until the early 1960s.

Data
Power plant: None
Wing span: 18.90 m (62 ft)
Wing area, gross: 22.29 m² (240 sq ft)
Wing aspect ratio: 16
Length overall: 8.18 m (26 ft 10 in)
Weight empty: 363 kg (800 lb)
Max t/o weight: 544 kg (1,200 lb)
Maximum diving speed: about 117 knots (217 km/h; 135 mph)
Min sinking speed: 0.7 m/sec (2.3 ft/sec) at 33 knots (61 km/h; 38 mph)

Variant
Nimbus. Single example only, registered BGA470.

Nimbus in tow during a gliding competition

S.44/S.A.6 SEALAND

First flight: 22 January 1948

Type: Twin-engined light commercial and military amphibian flying-boat
Notes and Structure: The Sealand was one of three new flying-boats projected by Shorts for postwar

Two Sealands destined for Jugoslovenski Aero Transport (JAT) of Yugoslavia, flying with G-AKLV that later went to Bengal

use but the only one of these built. In 1946 Shorts was heavily committed to the conversion of large military flying-boats to commercial configuration and the future for this type of aircraft looked promising, at least in the short term. To satisfy the market for small flying-boats, Shorts designed the S.A.6, which subsequently became known as the Sealand. The first example appeared in early 1948 and was the first new prototype from the Belfast factory, although Rochester had collaborated in its design. This was a flying-boat of neat design, its two 265 kW (355 hp) de Havilland Gipsy Queen Series 70 Mk II six-cylinder engines carried on high-mounted cantilever monoplane wings. The latter had an all-metal structure with Alclad stressed skin covering except for fabric on the flaps and ailerons. The wings had a parallel chord centre-section and tapering outer sections. Alclad also skinned the two-step hull, flush-riveted on the planing bottom only. The interchangeable welded Birmabright wingtip floats were carried on cantilever struts. The tail unit was conventional. Accommodation was provided for the pilot with single controls and five-to-seven passengers. An amphibious landing gear by Electro-Hydraulics was later fitted to the prototype G-AIVX.

The prototype Sealand was followed by four initial production-standard amphibians as Sealand Is, one of which took part in the 1949 King's Cup Air Race. These and subsequent Sealands were powered by two 254 kW (340 hp) Gipsy Queen

Series 70 Mk III engines (Gipsy Queen 70-3s). Following trials with early aircraft, extended wing-tips, a stronger hull and larger-area rudder became standard. A total of 25 Sealands was built, including the prototype. Most were flown overseas, foreign operators including the Indian Navy which took delivery of 10 with dual controls, extended endurance and Gipsy Queen 70-4 engines. Other operators included commercial airlines: two purchased by Vestlandske Flyselskap A/S of Norway to complement, or perhaps supersede, its fleet of four Republic Seabees and a Supermarine Walrus, were the only Sealands built (after the prototype in original form) in pure flying-boat configuration. Unlike the standard five-to-eight passenger Sealands, these, known as Sealand IIIs, had provision for ten passengers when no toilet compartment was fitted and had slightly better performance.

Data *(Sealand I)*
Accommodation: Pilot and five-to-eight passengers normally
Power plant: See NOTES
Wing span: 18.75 m (61 ft 6 in)

Wing area, gross: 33.32 m² (358.6 sq ft) with extended tips
Length overall: 12.85 m (42 ft 2 in)
Height (keel to top of rudder): 4.72 m (15 ft 6 in)
Weight empty: 3,204 kg (7,065 lb)
Max t/o weight: 4,128 kg (9,100 lb)
Max level speed: 162 knots (301 km/h; 187 mph)
Cruising speed: 153 knots (283 km/h; 176 mph) at 2,440 m (8,000 ft)
Max rate of climb at s/l: 305 m (1,000 ft)/min
Service ceiling: 6,340 m (20,800 ft)
Range with five passengers and baggage and 105 Imp gal of fuel: 409–517 nm (758–957 km; 471–595 miles)
Endurance: *(Indian Navy amphibians)* 6 h

Variants
S.44/S.A.6 Sealand I. Standard amphibious version. Total of 23 built including prototype.
S.B.2 Sealand II. Projected version with Alvis Leonides nine-cylinder radial engines of 336 kW (450 hp) and greater wing span. Not built.
S.B.7 Sealand III. Flying-boat version for service in Norway. Two only.

S.B.1

First flight: 14 July 1951

Type: Single-seat research glider
Notes and Structure: Shorts produced designs to fulfil both the B.14/46 bomber specification and the more important B.35/46, the former which led to the construction of the Sperrin and the latter as a contender to the V-bomber requirement. In the event the Short P.D.1 V-bomber project did not mature into a prototype, leaving Handley Page, Avro and Vickers to pick up production contracts for their Victor, Vulcan and Valiant respectively. The P.D.1 was, nevertheless, an important post-war project for Short Brothers and envisaged a large four-engined bomber with an aero-isoclinic wing as proposed by David Keith-Lucas, Short's chief designer.

The aero-isoclinic wing, instead of being stiff, was a relatively flexible structure. The all-moving tips, which comprised about one-fifth of the total wing area, served as both ailerons and elevators and made it possible to dispense with the normal tailplane and elevators. It was expected that the rotating tip controls would prove markedly superior to flap-type controls at transonic speeds and would make the aircraft more manoeuvrable at high altitudes.

In order to test the aero-isoclinic wing, Shorts produced its S.B.1. This was a glider representing a one-third aerodynamic scale model of the pro-

Tom Brooke-Smith in the cockpit of the S.B.1 in July 1951

jected P.D.1. Built at Belfast, it was first winch launched in mid-July 1951 and then on the 30th was towed into the air behind the prototype Short Sturgeon TT.Mk 2 tug. A further launch behind the Sturgeon on 14 October ended in disaster, when the S.B.1 crashed, badly injuring the pilot. It was thereafter rebuilt as the S.B.4 (which see).

Data
Power plant: None
Wing span: about 11.58 m (38 ft)
Length overall: Slightly shorter than Sherpa

Variant
S.B.1. Single example only, as described above.

S.A.4 SPERRIN

First flight: 10 August 1951

Type: Four turbojet medium-range bomber
Notes and Structure: The Sperrin was Short Brothers' first and only attempt at building a jet bomber of its own design, although the company subsequently built English Electric Canberras under contract. It was a bold venture, conceived to fulfil Ministry of Supply Specification B.14/46 as an Avro Lincoln replacement at a time when Britain had only jet fighter experience. This was a much more difficult specification than B.3/45, to which the Canberra was designed, which required a high-speed but light tactical bomber. B.14/46 called for a five-crew pressurised medium bomber operating on four Rolls-Royce Avon turbojets, capable of delivering a 10,000 lb bomb at a combat radius of 1,500 nm (2,780 km; 1,727 miles) and to possess a range of 3,500 nm (6,486 km;

4,030 miles) while armed with a nuclear weapon. It was also to be capable of high altitude bombing, at up to 13,715 m (45,000 ft) but, because of its high altitude performance, was not required to carry defensive armament. The maximum warload was to be 9,072 kg (20,000 lb) and cruising speed 434 knots (805 km/h; 500 mph).

Construction of the S.A.4 prototypes VX158 and VX161 began in 1948 and Short Brothers can rightly claim to have been the first British company to work on a four-jet bomber that flew, to the first such specification. However, construction and ground trials took a considerable period of time and the Vickers Valiant, built to the later and refined V-bomber specification, became the first British four-jet bomber to fly.

The first S.A.4 to fly was VX158, powered by four Rolls-Royce Avon RA.2 turbojet engines, each of 26.7 kN (6,000 lb static thrust). The second S.A.4 made its maiden flight just over a year

Sperrins VX158 and VX161, the former nearest the camera

VX158 flying with a Gyron turbojet engine installed in the enlarged lower port nacelle

later, on 12 August 1952, powered by improved 29 kN (6,500 lb static thrust) RA.3 turbojets. However, even before VX161 flew, the Vickers bomber had been selected for production.

VX158 completed its flight trials in the spring of 1953, by which time it was clear that the Short bomber would be required to fulfil only experimental roles. This situation was well summed up by the 1953–54 *Jane's All the World's Aircraft* which stated 'Although the S.A.4 is unlikely to go into production it does incorporate several important developments and ideas, particularly in

construction and in connection with flying controls, and is fully capable of carrying the large loads demanded by modern operational requirements. Its usefulness is therefore likely to be in the research field, where a large high-speed weight-carrying aircraft is needed for the investigation of the many problems associated with all aspects of modern bomber design, equipment and operation'. In fact VX158 was flown at the Royal Aircraft Establishment to assist in the development of a high-altitude radar blind-bombing system for Britain's forthcoming Valiant, Vulcan and Victor bombers and for flight testing (from 7 July 1955) the 66.7 kN (15,000 lb static thrust) de Havilland Gyron axial-flow turbojet engine (first run on 5 January 1953), installed in the lower port engine nacelle. A second Gyron was later installed in the same Sperrin. The cancellation of the Gyron programme also marked the end of the line for VX158, VX161 having already been grounded after one of its undercarriage doors had been removed to replace that lost earlier from VX158. However, before being grounded, VX161 had assisted in the development of a British nuclear stand-off missile to be carried by later V-bombers, its part played by dropping heavy representations of weapons. VX161 was the only Sperrin capable of carrying a heavy dummy or actual weapon.

The Sperrin had always been viewed only as an interim bomber. Despite good handling and a performance above that required, it had fallen foul of German-type technologies incorporated into the V-bombers. It was certainly unremarkable in

VX158 with two Gyron engines, first flown in this configuration on 26 June 1956

appearance, with the exception of its unusual engine arrangement with paired engines one above the other, an arrangement also tried in the Soviet Union by Sukhoi on its uncompleted Su-10 prototype of 1948. The Sperrin's fuselage was in three sections but constructed as one, the forward section containing the pressure cabin for the crew. The AD.7 aerofoil section wings were straight and tapered, with 1 degree of dihedral. As mentioned in the *Jane's* report, the Sperrin was the first British aircraft with full-span servo tabs on the trailing edges of the ailerons, elevators and rudder to move the surfaces aerodynamically.

Data
Power plant: See NOTES
Wing span: 33.22 m (109 ft)
Wing area, gross: 176.21 m² (1,896.72 sq ft)
Length overall: 31.18 m (102 ft 2.58 in)

Height overall: 8.69 m (28 ft 6¼ in)
Weight empty: 32,659 kg (72,000 lb)
Max weapon load: 9,072 kg (20,000 lb)
Max t/o weight: 52,163 kg (115,000 lb)
Max level speed: 490 knots (908 km/h; 564 mph) at 4,570 m (15,000 ft)
Cruising speed: 435 knots (806 km/h; 500 mph)
Service ceiling: 13,715 m (45,000 ft)
Range: 3,352 nm (6,212 km; 3,860 miles) with a 10,000 lb payload
Armament: Intended to carry a nuclear stand-off missile, a 10,000 lb bomb, or up to 9,072 kg (20,000 lb) of smaller bombs.

Variant
S.A.4 Sperrin. Two prototypes built, used as testbeds for military equipment and Gyron engines. The last broken up in 1958. Third airframe built for structural testing.

ENGLISH ELECTRIC CANBERRA

First flight; (Short-built) 30 October 1952

Type: Three-seat tactical light bomber, photographic reconnaissance and drone target aircraft
Notes and Structure: The Canberra was the first jet bomber to be built in the UK and the first to enter RAF service. The prototype made its first flight at Warton, Lancashire, on 13 May 1949. Production in the United Kingdom was undertaken by English Electric, Avro, Handley Page and Short Brothers & Harland. The latter concern produced sixty Canberra B.Mk 2s plus 72 Canberra B.Mk 6s, Canberra B(I). Mk 8s and PR.Mk 9s, all of which are described under VARIANTS.

Shorts was also responsible for developing the Canberra U.Mk 10, a pilotless target drone mainly for use at the Weapons Research Establishment at Woomera, Australia. Twenty-four U.Mk 10s were completed by conversion of retired B.Mk 2s, followed by six improved U.Mk 14s. Also, one PR.Mk 9 was modified by Shorts in 1960 to house infra-red equipment in a revised nose to assist in the Red Top air-to-air missile programme and a PR.Mk 3 was modified to become a launch aircraft for the Shorts-adapted Beechcraft AQM-37A supersonic target drone (40 of which were delivered from America in Model 1095 form). The modified AQM-37A was given the type designation S.D.2 by Shorts.

Since production of the Canberra ended in 1962, Shorts has maintained a strong association with the aircraft by the conversion, refurbishment and servicing of more than 100 Canberras under Ministry of Defence contract. However, in 1983 Shorts won a £3.5 million contract from the MoD to refurbish five PR.Mk 9s belonging to the RAF. This work will run until mid-1987. As well as covering reconditioning of the aircraft and servicing, the contract allows for new component

RAF Canberra PR.Mk 9

manufacture and the introduction of modifications designed by the company. The five aircraft are intended for long-range battlefield radar surveillance duties, to provide intelligence information in the battle zone and beyond. Each will carry the Ferranti Radar Systems data acquisition system Corps Airborne Standoff Radar (CASTOR).

Data *(Canberra B.Mk 2)*
Power plant: Two 28.91 kN (6,500 lb st) Rolls-Royce Avon 101 turbojet engines
Wing span: 19.49 m (63 ft 11½ in)
Length overall: 19.96 m (65 ft 6 in)
Height overall: 4.75 m (15 ft 7 in)
Max t/o weight: 20,865 kg (46,000 lb)
Max level speed: 449 knots (832 km/h; 517 mph)
Max rate of climb at s/l: 1,160 m (3,800 ft)/min
Max range with full bombload: 2,306 nm (4,274 km; 2,656 miles)
Armament: Up to 2,722 kg (6,000 lb) of bombs; typically six 1,000 lb bombs, or one 4,000 lb and two 1,000 lb bombs, or eight 500 lb bombs carried internally and 2,000 lb of bombs carried under the wings. Nuclear weapons an option.

Variants (built by Shorts)
Canberra B.Mk 2. As detailed above. Built also by English Electric, Avro and Handley Page.
Canberra B.Mk 6. Two 33 kN (7,400 lb st) Rolls-Royce Avon 109 turbojets. Gross weight of 24,948 kg (55,000 lb); maximum speed 504 knots (933 km/h; 580 mph); and range of 3,291 nm (6,100 km; 3,790 miles). Built also by English Electric.
Canberra B(I).Mk 8. Long-range night interdictor or high-altitude bomber and target marker version. Same power plant as B.Mk 6. Max level speed 470 knots (871 km/h; 541 mph). Armament of four 20 mm guns in underfuselage pack, two 1,000 lb bombs or (later) AS.30 missiles underwing, and three internally stowed 1,000 lb bombs.
Canberra PR.Mk 9. High-altitude photographic reconnaissance aircraft. Wing span increased by 1.22 m (4 ft) and wing centre-section chord inboard of nacelles extended. Offset canopy. Navigator's station in nose (with ejector seat), the extremity of which was hinged for entry. Power operated controls. Avon 206 turbojets. Built by Shorts, the prototype of which flew initially in July 1958. Five being modified as CASTOR PR. Mk 9s.
Canberra U.Mk 10. Unmanned target drone, suitable for operation at heights of up to 15,240 m (50,000 ft). Produced by conversion of B.Mk 2s. Controlled from ground by radio link. Total of 24 aircraft.
Canberra U.Mk 14. Improved target drone, used in Malta for Seacat missile trials.

Canberra U.Mk 10 target drone flown at the Woomera weapons range

S.B.5

First flight: 2 December 1952

Type: Research aircraft to investigate problems associated with the low-speed handling characteristics of sweptback wings.

Notes and Structure: The single-seat S.B.5 was constructed to provide data for the projected English Electric P.1 prototype fighter and was responsible for all the low-speed research carried out in the development of this aircraft. Short designed the S.B.5 to enable varying degrees of wing sweepback to be tested. The tailplane could also be re-positioned, either at the extreme top of the fin or beneath the rear fuselage, and its angle of incidence was variable. The varying degrees of wing sweepback were achieved by fitting alternative components and four configurations could be tested. These were 50° wing sweepback with a high tail unit; 60° sweepback with a low tail unit; 60° sweepback with a high tail unit; and 69° sweepback with a low tail unit.

The angle of incidence of the tailplane could be varied in flight from 10° above to 10° below the horizontal. The position of the tricycle landing gear could also be altered to enable each configuration to be tested at various C.G. positions.

The S.B.5 completed a series of tests with 50°

and 60° sweepback while powered by the Rolls-Royce Derwent engine, but was re-engined with a Bristol Siddeley Orpheus turbojet to test the 69° configuration, in which form it began flying again on 18 October 1960. The aircraft finished its days at the Empire Test Pilots' School at Farnborough, where it was used to gain experience in flying short-span aircraft at low speeds.

Data

Power plant: One 15.57 kN (3,500 lb st) Rolls-Royce Derwent turbojet engine. Later one 21.57 kN (4,850 lb st) Bristol Siddeley Orpheus BOr.3 turbojet engine.

Wing span: *(50° wing configuration)* 10.72 m (35 ft 2¼ in); *(60° wing configuration)* 9.30 m (30 ft 6 in); *(69° wing configuration)* 7.92 m (25 ft 11¾ in)

Wing area, gross: *(50° wing configuration)* 25.37 m² (273.1 sq ft); *(60° wing configuration)* 25.72 m² (276.9 sq ft); *(69° wing configuration)* 26.17 m² (281.7 sq ft)

Length overall: 13.94 m (45 ft 9 in)

Height overall: *(high tailplane)* 5.05 m (16 ft 7 in); *(low tailplane)* 4.57 m (15 ft)

Weight empty: 4,171 kg (9,196 lb)

Max t/o weight: 5,443 kg (12,000 lb)

Max level speed: 287 knots (500 km/h; 311 mph)

Variant

S.B.5. Single research aircraft with serial number WG768.

S.B.5 with high tailplane and 50° of wing sweepback

S.B.5, photographed in 1960, with a low-mounted tailplane, 69° of wing sweepback and the Bristol Siddeley Orpheus engine installed

S.B.6 SEAMEW

First flight: 23 August 1953

Type: Two-seat lightweight anti-submarine aircraft

Notes and Structure: During the 1940s and 1950s the FAA received production examples of two entirely different aircraft bearing the name Seamew, neither of which became operational in their intended role. The first was the wartime Curtiss Seamew; some 100 were received from America under Lend-Lease as armed reconnaissance aircraft for catapult-launching from warships. Because of poor handling characteristics, FAA Curtiss Seamews were used only as aircrew train-

ers. The second Seamew type came from Shorts.

Designed to fulfil Specification M.123, the Short Seamew was a lightweight anti-submarine aircraft, designed for operation from escort carriers and small coastal airfields. It was among the first postwar aircraft to veer towards simplicity and was therefore expected to be cheaper and quicker to manufacture than any postwar front-line military aircraft up to that time. It was a limited all-weather type of unusual configuration, with search and strike capability. A mid-wing monoplane with a non-retractable tailwheel-type undercarriage, it carried a crew comprising the pilot in a high cockpit with excellent vision and a navigator to his rear in a separate cockpit. Under the forward fuselage was carried a radar scanner, while internal stowage was provided for 20 sonobuoys or four depth-charges. Rockets and marine markers were carried beneath the folding wings. Power was provided by a 1,230 kW (1,650 shp) Armstrong Siddeley Mamba ASMa.6 turboprop engine in production examples, the engine weighing 431 kg (951 lb).

The first of two flying Seamew prototypes took off for its maiden flight on 23 August 1953, powered by a 977 kW (1,310 shp) ASMa.3 turboprop. An initial production order was placed in early 1955, covering 41 aircraft for the FAA as Seamew AS.Mk 1s and Mk 2s for Coastal Command, RAF, the latter with the carrier equipment deleted. However, the RAF examples were later cancelled. Delivery of production Seamew AS.Mk 1s began in 1956 but only a small number had been received by the FAA when the production programme was cancelled as part of a round of defence cuts. In the event no Seamews became operational and those flown proved difficult to handle.

Data
Power plant: See NOTES
Wing span: 16.76 m (55 ft)
Wing area, gross: 54.3 m² (585 sq ft)

Length overall: 12.50 m (41 ft)
Height overall: 4.09 m (13 ft 5 in)
Weight empty: 4,443 kg (9,795 lb)
Max t/o weight: (normal) 6,532 kg (14,400 lb); *(overload)* 6,804 kg (15,000 lb)
Max level speed at s/l: 204 knots (378 km/h; 235 mph) at 6,123 kg (13,500 lb) AUW; 202 knots (375 km/h; 233 mph) at 3,050 m (10,000 ft) at above AUW
Max rate of climb at s/l, max t/o weight: at 373 m (1,222 ft)/min
Range: 651 nm (1,207 km; 750 miles)
Endurance at 120 knots (222 km/h; 138 mph) at 1,525 m (5,000 ft), with full allowances for warm up, climb, descent and landing: 4.8 h
Armament: Sonobuoys, depth-charges, etc, up to 836 kg (1,844 lb)

Variants
S.B.6 Seamew prototypes. Two flying prototypes, powered by ASMa.3 turboprop engines.
Seamew AS.Mk 1. Production version for FAA, with ASMa.6 turboprop engine. None became operational.

The second prototype Seamew lands on HMS *Bulwark* during acceptance trials

The first production Seamew AS.Mk 1 with wings folded

S.B.4 SHERPA

First flight: 4 October 1953

Type: Single-seat powered research aircraft to investigate the possibilities of the aero-isoclinic wing

Notes and Structure: The Sherpa was basically a powered version of the S.B.1, constructed after the crash of the glider and built with a new fuselage and other changes. The wings, rebuilt from the S.B.1, had an aspect ratio of 5.6, anhedral of 1° and sweepback of 42° 22′. Its flexural axis was located well aft and torsional stiffness was so adjusted that sufficient nose-up twist was provided to cancel out aerodynamic warping due to flexure. To assist this, wingtip elevons were used in place of the usual wing trailing-edge controls. These elevons, which were hinged at 30 per cent chord, could be rotated either together or differentially, to act as elevators or ailerons respectively. The wing structure was mainly of spruce and plywood, light alloy being

adopted only in strategic positions. An electrically actuated anti-balance tab was inset at the inboard end of the trailing-edge of each elevon. Landing flaps were inset in the underside of the wings. No tailplane was fitted and the tailfin and rudder were swept. Air intakes for the engines were flush on the fuselage deck, with jet efflux pipes on the sides of the fuselage aft of the wings. The fuselage itself was a stressed-skin light alloy structure in the centre position, the tail position being constructed of spruce frames and continuous stringers and plywood bulkheads and skins, and the nose of resin-impregnated glassfibre split horizontally so that the upper and lower sections could be removed easily to give access to equipment carried in the nose.

On completion of its test programme with Shorts, the Sherpa was given to the College of Aeronautics at Cranfield where, barring a period of engine trouble that brought a halt to flying during 1958–60, it was flown until 1964, proving easy to handle in flight. It was then sent as a ground test

Sherpa research aircraft. The flush air intakes in the upper fuselage and the jetpipes emerging from above the trailing edges of the wings can be seen. The engines themselves were inclined outwards by 10° to the centreline of the fuselage

aircraft to the Bristol College of Advanced Technology and finished up at the Skyfame Aircraft Museum at Staverton.

Data
Power plant: Two 1.47 kN (330 lb st) Blackburn-built Turboméca Palas turbojet engines
Wing span: 11.58 m (38 ft)
Wing area, gross: 21.37 m² (230 sq ft)

Length overall: 9.70 m (31 ft 10 in)
Height overall: 2.77 m (9 ft 1 in)
Weight empty: 1,361 kg (3,000 lb)
Max t/o weight: up to 1,482 kg (3,268 lb)
Max level speed: 148 knots (274 km/h; 170 mph)
Endurance: 50 mins

Variant
S.B.4 Sherpa. Single example used for research purposes. Carried marking G-14-I.

S.C.1

First flight: 2 April 1957

Type: VTOL research aircraft
Notes and Structure: Developed to official Specification ER143, the S.C.1 was the first fixed-wing VTOL aeroplane to be built in the UK. Design began in 1954 and construction in 1955, and the first of two S.C.1s made its maiden flight from Boscombe Down on 2 April 1957 using normal take-off techniques. The second aircraft made the first tethered vertical hovering flight on 23 May 1958. A series of hovering trials in a specially designed test gantry was followed by free vertical take-offs from an open platform, the first taking place on 25 October 1958.

The maiden vertical flight by the first aircraft was performed on 20 July 1960, but the first complete transition from vertical to forward horizontal flight and vice versa had already been accomplished by the second S.C.1 on 6 April 1960. In May 1961 the first S.C.1 became the first jet-lift aircraft to fly the English Channel but on 2 October 1963 the second S.C.1 crashed from a low altitude and the pilot was killed (after 81 flights with the Mk 3 auto-stabiliser – see below). It was thereafter rebuilt and joined the first at the Royal Aircraft Establishment, Bedford, in 1967. There both aircraft were used for exhaustive research into the

145

S.C.1 with its four lift engines showing within the fuselage centre-section

landing characteristics of VTOL aircraft.

The S.C.1 itself was a small aircraft with delta wings and a vertical tail unit only. Its landing gear was of non-retractable tricycle type, the main legs of which were pivoted and could be moved hydraulically through 15° fore-and-aft, enabling the wheels to be positioned further aft of C.G. during vertical landing. Four of the five engines were used to provide jet-lift and were mounted vertically in cross-wise pairs, each pair swinging on a transverse axis: after vertical take-off the engines were inclined rearward to give added forward thrust, and before vertical landing they could be directed forward to give a braking effect. The fifth engine exhausted horizontally at the tail for thrust in forward flight. All the engines had a compressor bleed, supplying high-pressure air to a common duct which fed control nozzles at the wingtips, nose and tail. The second S.C.1 differed from the first in being fitted with a Mk 3 auto-stabiliser.

Data

Accommodation: Pilot only
Power plant: Five 9.47 kN (2,130 lb st) Rolls-Royce RB.108 turbojet engines
Wing span: 7.16 m (23 ft 6 in)
Wing area, gross: 13.18 m² (141.9 sq ft)
Length overall: 9.11 m (29 ft 10 in)
Height overall: 3.25 m (10 ft 8 in)
Weight empty: 2,722 kg (6,000 lb)
Max t/o weight: 3,650 kg (8,050 lb)
Max level speed: 214 knots (396 km/h; 246 mph)
Service ceiling: 2,440 m (8,000 ft)
Range with max fuel and max payload: 130 nm (240 km; 150 miles)

Variant

S.C.1. Two prototypes, designated XG900 and XG905.

Second S.C.1 fitted with the Mk 3 auto-stabiliser, leaving the specially prepared take-off platform

One of several design studies undertaken by Shorts for VTOL combat planes was this, the PD 25 ground attack aircraft

BRISTOL TYPE 175 BRITANNIA

First flight: (Short-built) 1 June 1957

Type: Four-engined airliner and military transport
Notes and Structure: On 16 August 1952 the prototype Bristol Britannia airliner made its first flight at Filton. The initial production version was the Britannia 102, of which 15 had been ordered for BOAC. The first two of these were used to gain the C of A (the first having flown on 15 September 1954) and thereafter were handed over to Shorts for modification to airline standard for commercial use. On 1 February 1957 BOAC made its first use of turboprop-powered airliners, by introducing the Britannia on its London–Johannesburg route. Power was provided by four Bristol Siddeley Proteus 705 engines and accommodation was provided for 92 tourist class passengers or 60 first class passengers.

In 1956 Short began actual manufacture of Britannias under Bristol sub-contract, the models built by Shorts being listed under VARIANTS.

Data
Accommodation: See NOTES and VARIANTS
Power plant: See NOTES and VARIANTS
Wing span: 43.35 m (142 ft 3½ in)
Length overall: (*Britannia 252, 253, 302, 305 and 314*) 37.87 m (124 ft 3 in)
Height overall: (*Britannia 252, 253, 302, 305 and 314*) 11.43 m (37 ft 6 in)
Weight empty: (*252*) 42,638 kg (94,000 lb); (*253*) 40,029 kg (88,250 lb); (*302*) 41,957 kg (92,500 lb); (*305*) 41,050 kg (90,500 lb)
Max payload: (*252 and 305*) 12,700 kg (28,000 lb); (*253*) 15,422 kg (34,000 lb); (*302*)

13,608 kg (30,000 lb); (*314*) 15,845 kg (34,900 lb)
Max t/o weight: (*252, 253 and 305*) 81,646 kg (180,000 lb); (*302*) 74,842 kg (165,000 lb); (*314*) 83,990 kg (185,000 lb)
Cruising speed at 63,400 kg (140,000 lb) AUW: 350 knots (648 km/h; 403 mph)
Range with max payload: (*252*) 3,908 nm (7,420 km; 4,500 miles) at 310 knots (575 km/h; 357 mph); (*253*) 3,890 nm (7,210 km; 4,480 miles) at 310 knots (575 km/h; 357 mph); (*302*) 2,987 nm (5,536 km; 3,440 miles) at 310 knots (575 km/h; 357 mph); (*305*) 4,194 nm (7,773 km; 4,830 miles) at 310 knots (575 km/h; 357 mph); (*314*) 3,706 nm (6,867 km; 4,268 miles) at 310 knots (575 km/h; 357 mph)

Variants (built by Shorts only)
Britannia 252. Three aircraft ordered from Short Brothers & Harland by the Ministry of Supply and subsequently used by the RAF (Air Transport Command). These became long-range trooping aircraft and freighters. Forward fuselage only had reinforced floor, and a new large loading door for freight was provided. The remainder of the fuselage was of similar layout to civil aircraft. Maximum troop accommodation was 99, or 22 stretchers and 39 sitting casualties could be carried in air ambulance role. First flown at Belfast on 3 October 1958, with first aircraft handed over to the RAF on 21 March 1959.
Britannia 253. Total of 20 built for the RAF as Britannia C.Mk 1 long-range all-purpose transports. Strengthened floor throughout fuselage length. Large freight door, as for 252, plus 'floating' freight door and special loading lift. Accommodation for 115 troops on rearward-facing seats, or 53 stretchers plus six attendants, or all freight. Quickly removable seats stowed in lower freight hold when not in use. As Britannia 252, powered by four 3,315 ekW (4,445 ehp) Bristol Siddeley Proteus 255 turboprops. Fifteen built by Short Brothers & Harland and five assembled from Short-built components by Bristol Aircraft. First Britannia C.Mk 1 flew at Belfast on 29 December 1958.
Britannia 302. First production version of the 300 Series. Two completed for Aeronaves de Mexico by Short Brothers & Harland.
Britannia 305. Five aircraft, built by Short Brothers & Harland. Similar to 302 but with strengthened wings and Series 310 wing fuel tankage for long-range operation. Ordered for Northeast Airlines but later cancelled. Two taken over by the Argentine carrier Transcontinental SA.
Britannia 314. Five Series 310 aircraft built by Short Brothers & Harland for Canadian Pacific Airlines. As for Britannia 302 and 305, fitted with

RAF Air Transport Command Britannia C.Mk 1 *Argo*, built by Short Brothers & Harland Ltd. at Belfast

either four 3,072 ekW (4,120 ehp) Proteus 755 or 3,315 ekW (4,445 ehp) Proteus 765 turboprop engines.

Additional Notes
Shorts also undertook postwar the manufacture of de Havilland Comet 2 and Vickers VC10 fuselages, plus components for other aircraft including the McDonnell Douglas Phantom II (Royal Navy F-4K version) and the Fokker F28 Fellowship airliner, the latter which continues. As these were not completed aircraft, none are individually listed.

S.C.7 SKYVAN

First flight: 17 January 1963

Type: STOL utility light transport
Notes and Structure: Design of the Skyvan began as a private venture in 1959 and construction of a prototype was started in the following year. This aircraft, powered by two 290 kW (390 hp) Continental GTSIO-520 piston engines, completed its flight trials by mid-1963 and was then re-engined with two Turboméca 388 kW (520 shp) Astazou II turboprop engines. In this form it flew for the first time on 2 October 1963; with Rolls-Royce Continental engines the prototype was known as the Skyvan Series 1, changing designation to Series 1A with Astazous. Details of the following production types can be found under VARIANTS. In February 1970 the Skyvan became the first aircraft to be certificated under the British Air Regulation Board's new Civil Airworthiness Requirements for STOL operations.

The Skyvan is a braced high-wing light transport, equally suited to passenger or troop/paratroop, freight or vehicle carrying. Its main feature is the square-section fuselage, which has an internal main cabin height and width of 1.98 m (6 ft 6 in). The aircraft carries its own lightweight

Production Skyvan Series 2, bought by Olympic Airways for Greek inter-island flights

Skyvan Series 3 specially equipped for aerial surveys

vehicle loading ramps and has a one-piece door which leaves the fuselage threshold completely clear of obstructions during through loading. The landing gear is of non-retractable nosewheel type and a twin fin and rudder tail unit is provided.

By early 1983 the total number of orders and options for the Skyvan had reached 150, of which 56 represented Series 3 and 3M orders for service with several air forces plus the Argentinian Naval Prefectura, Lesotho Police, Malawi Police and Royal Thai Police. Three of six for the Singapore Air Force are equipped for search and rescue missions and the three for the Indonesian Air Force are to civil standard and operate social services for the Ministry of the Interior.

Data

Accommodation: *(Series 3)* Up to 19 passengers or 12 stretcher patients and medical attendants, or 2,085 kg (4,600 lb) of freight, vehicles or agricultural equipment; *(Series 3M)* up to 22 equipped troops, 16 paratroops and a dispatcher, 12 stretchers and two attendants, or 2,358 kg (5,200 lb) of freight.

Power plant: *(Series 1 and 1A)* See NOTES; *(Series 2)* two 514.5 kW (690 shp) Turboméca Astazou XII turboprop engines; *(Series 3, 3A, 3M, 3M-200 and Skyliner)* Two 533 kW (715 shp) Garrett TPE331-201 turboprop engines.

Wing span: 19.79 m (64 ft 11 in)

Wing area, gross: 34.65 m² (373 sq ft)

Length overall: *(without radome)* 12.21 m (40 ft 1 in); *(with radome)* 12.60 m (41 ft 4 in)

Height overall: 4.60 m (15 ft 1 in)

Basic operating weight: *(Series 2)* 3,435 kg (7,575 lb); *(Series 3)* 3,331 kg (7,344 lb); *(Series 3M)* 3,356 kg (7,400 lb); *(Series 3M-200, equipped)* 3,768 kg (8,307 lb)

Max payload for normal t/o weight: *(Series 2 and 3)* 2,086 kg (4,600 lb); *(Series 3M and 3M-200)* 2,358 kg (5,200 lb)

Max t/o weight: *(Series 2 and 3, normal)* 5,670 kg (12,500 lb); *(3M, normal)* 6,214 kg (13,700 lb); *(3M-200)* 6,804 kg (15,000 lb)

Max cruising speed at 3,050 m (10,000 ft): *(Series 2)* 169 knots (314 km/h; 195 mph); *(Series 3 and 3M)* 175 knots (324 km/h; 202 mph), at max continuous power; *(Series 3M-200)* 174 knots (322 km/h; 200 mph) at 6,577 kg (14,500 lb) AUW

Max rate of climb at s/l: *(Series 2)* 442 m (1,450 ft)/min; *(Series 3)* 500 m (1,640)/min; *(Series 3M)* 466 m (1,530 ft)/min

Service ceiling: *(Series 2)* 6,100 m (20,000 ft); *(Series 3)* 6,858 m (22,500 ft); *(Series 3M)* 6,705 m (22,000 ft)

Range at long-range cruising speed, 45 min reserves: *(Series 2 and 3)* 600 nm (1,115 km; 694 miles); *(Series 3M)* 580 nm (1,075 km; 670 miles); *(Series 2)* 338 nm (628 km; 390 miles) with a 1,814 kg (4,000 lb) payload; *(Series 3, as typical freighter)* 162 nm (300 km; 187 miles) with a 1,814 kg (4,000 lb) payload, ISA; *(Series 3M, as typical freighter)* 208 nm (386 km; 240 miles) with a 2,268 kg (5,000 lb) payload, ISA; *(Series 3M-200)* 540 nm (1,000 km; 621 miles) with a 1,814 kg (4,000 lb) payload, ISA + 10°C

One of the Sultan of Oman's Air Force's sixteen Skyvan Series 3Ms, flown by No 2 Squadron

Variants

Skyvan Series 1. Prototype (G-ASCN) when fitted with Continental engines.

Skyvan Series 1A. Prototype as redesigned when fitted with Astazou II engines.

Skyvan Series 2. Three development aircraft and 16 initial production Skyvans, each fitted with Astazou XII engines. Several later re-engined to Series 3 standard. Production ended.

Skyvan Series 3. Current civil version, which superseded Series 2 in 1968. First Series 3 to fly was the second development aircraft (G-ASZI), which had been equipped originally with Astazous. First flight with Garrett engines was made on 15 December 1967, and a second aircraft (G-ASZJ) re-engined with TPE331s flew on 20 January 1968.

Skyvan Series 3A. Introduced in 1970 to comply with BCAR Passenger Transport Category, in Performance Group A: max t/o weight of 6,215 kg (13,700 lb); max landing weight of 6,075 kg (13,400 lb). Two ordered. Production completed.

Skyvan Series 3M. Military version of the Series 3, modified internally to accept optional equipment for typical military missions. The prototype (G-AXPT) first flew in 1970. Equipment includes port-side blister window for an air dispatcher; two anchor cables for parachute static lines; a guard rail beneath the tail to prevent control surface fouling by the static lines; inward facing paratroop seats with safety nets; parachute signal light;

Skyliner in the colours of Gulf Air

mounts for NATO-type stretchers; and roller conveyors for easy loading and paradropping of pallet mounted supplies.

Skyvan Series 3M-200. Skyvan cleared for operations in non-civil applications at a max t/o weight of 6,804 kg (15,000 lb).

Skyliner. De luxe all-passenger version of the Series 3/3A with a longer cabin. Nine sold. Production ended.

S.C.5 BELFAST

First flight: 5 January 1964

Type: Heavy long-range military transport

Notes and Structure: Originally known as the Britannic, the Belfast was developed as a military strategic transport to carry heavy freight, including the largest types of guns, vehicles (including tanks), helicopters, guided missiles and other loads with which the RAF and the British Army were concerned. Alternatively, the internal layout could be altered to allow the accommodation of 153 troops or more when using a removable upper floor.

Though looking very different, the Belfast was based upon the Britannia, which was then in production by Shorts. This included the use of the Britannia's wings, tail surfaces and systems, but these were married to a new fuselage of large dimensions with 'beaver tail' rear loading doors to

permit unhindered straight-through loading into the capacious hold and a large loading door on one side of the fuselage.

Intended for military and commercial use, despite considerable effort no sales of new aircraft for civil use was achieved. Production covered just 10 aircraft for the RAF. Each of these Belfast C.Mk 1s was powered by four 4,270 kW (5,730 ehp) Rolls-Royce Tyne RTy.12 turboprop engines. All ten entered service with No 53 Squadron from January 1966. The first true military task of the Belfast was to return Whirlwind helicopters and other equipment from Guyana and airlift Wessex helicopters to Cyprus. However, although still of major importance to the RAF, the Belfasts were withdrawn from military service in 1976 as one measure of a round of defence cutbacks. This effectively left the RAF with no heavy transport in service, a situation which remains today.

Apart from a straight commercial counterpart to the military Belfast, Shorts considered another

Maiden flight of the Belfast C.Mk 1 from Sydenham Airport, Belfast

derivative using a US Lockheed C-141 StarLifter-type wing and Rolls-Royce RB.178 turbojet engines. This too remained a project. But, ironically, ex-RAF Belfasts were offered for sale to commercial freight operators; Eurolatin Aviation purchased three and five were bought by TAC Heavy-Lift (now named HeavyLift Air Cargoes), thus making the aircraft a purely civil type. HeavyLift operates from London's Stansted Airport, its Belfasts entering commercial use in 1980 having been modified to the required standard by Marshall of Cambridge (Engineering) Ltd. The company's first charter operation with the Belfast required the transportation of two Bristow Helicopters' Westland Pumas to Perth, Australia. At the present time the airline flies three Belfasts, with the others in reserve.

Data
Accommodation: Military loads as mentioned above. HeavyLift's Belfasts carry up to 34,020 kg (75,000 lb) of freight
Power plant: See NOTES
Wing span: 48.40 m (158 ft 9½ in)
Wing area, gross: 229.10 m² (2,466 sq ft)
Length overall: 41.58 m (136 ft 5 in)
Height overall: 14.33 m (47 ft)
Weight empty: 56,699 kg (125,000 lb)
Max t/o weight: (*Belfast C.Mk 1*) 102,058 kg (225,000 lb); (*HeavyLift Belfast*) 104,325 kg (230,000 lb)
Cruising speed: (*Belfast C.Mk 1*) 306 knots (566 km/h; 352 mph); (*HeavyLift Belfast*) 274 knots (510 km/h; 316 mph)

Range: (*Belfast C.Mk 1*) 4,603 nm (8,530 km; 5,300 miles); (*HeavyLift Belfast*) 3,348 nm (6,205 km; 3,855 miles) with 10,000 kg (22,040 lb) payload; (*HeavyLift Belfast*) 847 nm (1,575 km; 975 miles) with full payload

Variants
Belfast C.Mk 1. Ten examples for No 53 Squadron, RAF, operated between 1966 and 1976.
Civil Belfast. No commercial Belfasts were built as new. Ex-RAF Belfasts were offered for sale, with five going to HeavyLift Air Cargoes.

A Saladin armoured car backs into a Belfast C.Mk 1

HeavyLift Air Cargoes' commercial Belfast transport

330 and SHERPA

First flight: (330) 22 August 1974

Type: Twin-turboprop transport

Notes and Structure: Originally known as the SD3-30, the Shorts 330 is a 30-passenger transport aircraft designed primarily for commuter and regional air service operators who require a modern aircraft offering greater seating capacity than available from previous aircraft in this category.

Derived from the Skyvan, the 330 retains many of the latter type's well proven characteristics, including the large cabin cross-section. The same safe-life concept and design philosophy is employed in the structural components.

Two prototypes and the first production aircraft were used for the development programme, the first prototype flying in August 1974. Eight days earlier, the first order for the 330 had been placed by Command Airways of Poughkeepsie, New York, for three aircraft. CAA certification to full Transport Category requirements was granted in February 1976 and this was followed by subsequent approvals from other countries, and the aircraft conforms with the latest US noise requirements. Initial deliveries began in June 1976 and the 330 first went into service with Time Air on 24 August 1976. By the beginning of 1984 orders and options for the 330 totalled 180, when the 94 in use had together carried more than 20 million passengers.

Three versions of the aircraft are available, including an all-freight variant known as the Sherpa. Details of these can be found under VARIANTS. Initial production 330s were powered by 862 kW (1,156 shp) Pratt & Whitney Aircraft of Canada PT6A-45B turboprop engines but current aircraft have two 893 kW (1,198 shp) PT6A-45R engines. The 330 is a strut-braced high-wing monoplane of light alloy construction, with a square-section fuselage giving an internal cabin width and height of 1.93 m (6 ft 4 in) 1.98 m (6 ft 6 in) for the Sherpa. The tail unit is a cantilever structure comprising a fixed-incidence tailplane and full-span elevator with twin fins and rudders. The wheels of the landing gear are retractable, the main units being carried on short sponsons into which they retract hydraulically.

153

Data

Accommodation: Standard seating for 30 passengers, with baggage compartment in the nose and rear of cabin. See VARIANTS.

Power plant: See NOTES

Wing span: 22.76 m (74 ft 8 in)

Wing area, gross: 42.1 m² (453 sq ft)

Length overall: 17.69 m (58 ft 0½ in)

Height overall: 4.95 m (16 ft 3 in)

Weight empty: *(330-200 for 30 passengers, including crew)* 6,680 kg (14,727 lb); *(Sherpa)* 6,680 kg (14,727 lb)

Max payload for normal t/o weight: *(330-200 with 30 passengers and baggage)* 2,653 kg (5,850 lb); *(330-200 with cargo)* 3,400 kg (7,500 lb); *(Sherpa)* 3,175 kg (7,000 lb)

Max t/o weight: 10,387 kg (22,900 lb)

Max cruising speed at 3,050 m (10,000 ft): *(330-200 and Sherpa)* 190 knots (352 km/h; 218 mph) at 9,525 kg (21,000 lb) AUW; *(330-UTT)* 201 knots (372 km/h; 231 mph) at 9,979 kg (22,000 lb) AUW

Max rate of climb at s/l: *(330-200 and Sherpa)* 360 m (1,180 ft)/min; *(330-UTT)* 381 m (1,250 ft)/min at t/o weight of 10,387 kg (22,900 lb)

One of the 330-200s in US service is this Golden West airliner

Range with 30 passengers, cruising at 3,050 m (10,000 ft), no reserves: 473 nm (876 km; 544 miles)

Range with max fuel: *(330-200 in passenger layout)* 915 nm (1,695 km; 1,053 miles) with cruising altitude of 3,050 m (10,000 ft) and no reserves; *(300-200 in cargo layout with a 2,306 kg; 5,085 lb payload)* 758 nm (1,403 km; 872 miles); *(Sherpa)* 195 nm (362 km; 225 miles) with a 3,175 kg (7,000 lb) payload and reserves; *(Sherpa)* 669 nm (1,239 km; 770 miles) with a 2,268 kg (5,000 lb) payload and reserves

Variants

330-200. Standard passenger version. Also available in mixed traffic layout with partition to divide the cabin into a rear passenger area (typically for 18 persons) and a forward cargo compartment. An all-cargo configuration can be adopted.

330-UTT. Announced in September 1982 that production of this military STOL utility tactical transport version had begun. Basically similar to the standard 330 but with the maximum payload increased to 3,630 kg (8,000 lb) and with a maximum necessity t/o weight of 11,158 kg (24,600 lb). Cabin accommodation can be provided for 33 troops, 30 paratroops plus a jumpmaster, or 15 stretchers plus four seated attendants.

The Sherpa demonstrating one of the rear ramp door loading positions

Sherpa. Freighter version of 330, retaining many features of the passenger version to allow utility passenger operations, but featuring a Skyvan type full-width rear cargo door for through loading as well as the standard forward freight door and wide-body hold of all versions. The hydraulically actuated rear ramp door can be lowered to a variety of positions to simplify loading from a wide range of ground equipment. Standard airline containers can be accommodated in the main cabin, up

to the size of the LD3, making the Sherpa particularly suited for the operation of short-haul cargo feeder services. The prototype first flew on 23 December 1982 and production aircraft have been completed.

C-23. US Air Force designation for 18 Sherpas ordered in March 1984 for the EDSA (European Distribution Supply Aircraft) role in Europe. These will be based at Zweibrücken, West Germany, for transportation of high priority spares between USAF bases in Europe. Forty-eight more C-23s on option. Deliveries to begin in August 1984.

360

First flight: 1 June 1981

Type: Twin-turboprop commuter transport
Notes and Structure: The 360 is a development of the 330, seating six extra passengers in the lengthened fuselage and having strengthened outer wing panels and bracing struts, a new tail unit with a single fin and rudder, and new more-powerful engines with improved fuel economy.

Designed specifically for short-haul airline operations over typical commuter average stage lengths of about 120 nm (222 km; 138 miles), the

360 retains the basic configuration of the 330 except in the details noted above. As for the 330 and Skyvan, pressurisation is considered unnecessary in view of the short stage lengths over which the aircraft operates, and this enables the aircraft to retain the same 'walkabout' headroom, square section wide-bodied interior, seating comfort, air-conditioning and other amenities as its predecessor. Because of the availability of more baggage space, each of the 36 passengers can use a baggage volume of 0.20 m³ (7 cu ft), which Shorts claim is unique among current commuter aircraft.

The prototype 360 (G-ROOM) appeared six months ahead of schedule and flew in mid-1981.

Shorts 360 before delivery to Simmons Air of Michigan

This was powered by PT6A-45 engines, but production aircraft use two 990 kW (1,327 shp) Pratt & Whitney Aircraft of Canada PT6A-65R turboprops, each driving an advanced technology propeller. The first production 360 made its maiden flight on 19 August 1982 and entered commercial service with Suburban Airlines of Pennsylvania on 1 December 1982. Orders and options for the 360 totalled 90 by March 1984.

Data
Accommodation: Up to 36 passengers
Power plant: See NOTES
Wing span: 22.81 m (74 ft 10 in)
Wing area, gross: 42.1 m² (453 sq ft)
Length overall: 21.59 m (70 ft 10 in)

Height overall: 7.21 m (23 ft 8 in)
Operating weight empty: *(cargo)* 7,183 kg (15,835 lb); *(36 passengers)* 7,666 kg *(16,900 lb)*
Max payload: *(36 passengers and baggage)* 3,184 kg (7,020 lb); *(cargo)* 3,765 kg (8,300 lb)
Max t/o weight: 11,793 kg (26,000 lb)
Cruising speed at max recommended cruise power: 212 knots (393 km/h; 244 mph)
Range at 3,050 m (10,000 ft), cruising at 212 knots (393 km/h; 244 mph), no reserves (36 passengers): 435 nm (806 km; 501 miles)
Range, conditions as above with max fuel: 916 nm (1,697 km; 1,055 miles)

Variant
360. 36-passenger commuter airliner, as described above.

Index

157

160